Mort's Guide™ to Low-Cost Vacations & Lodgings On College Campuses

USA, & Canada

By Mort Barish and Michaela M. Mole

Research and Editorial Staff:
Deirdre Adams, Sally Kollmar, Abigail Houston

CMG PUBLISHING CO., INC., P.O. Box 630, Princeton, N.J. 08540

I

Printed in the United States
of America

Library of Congress Catalog Card
Number 74-82872

ISBN 0-9600718-2-2

First Printing by CMG, November 1974

Although the publisher has exhaus-
tively researched all sources to insure
the accuracy and completeness of the
information contained in this Guide,
we assume no responsibility for
errors, inaccuracies, omissions, avail-
ability of lodgings, or any other
inconsistency contained herein.

Get in on the World's Best Kept Secret.
Out of the 8,000 colleges and universities in the world, 300 in 46 countries welcome travelers and vacationers. To stay a day, a weekend or longer. In beautiful two-in-a-room accommodations. Rates are so incredibly low, they're hard to believe. $1.00 to $5.00 a day. You get to use the college's sports, recreational, and cultural facilities free. Tennis, swimming, music, art, libraries, dance...everything that happens on a college campus is yours for the asking. Open to everyone. Not just students.

There's only one place to find out all about it. In MORT'S GUIDE TO LOW COST VACATIONS & LODGINGS on COLLEGE CAMPUSES. There's an International Edition and another covering the USA & Canada.

Can you imagine? Overnight accommodations at a university in Yugoslavia for 44¢ a day. New York City $5.00 a day. France $2.52 a day. New Orleans $2.75 a day. Egypt $1.50 a day. Plus 300 more locations to choose from at comparable rates.

Eat at the university coffee shop or cafeteria. 85¢ is average for breakfast. $1.25 for lunch. $1.75 for dinner.

Pursue Your Hobby or Avocation: Rock collecting, bird watching, photography, native arts and crafts.

If You Seek Cultural Attractions, you can "go by the book:" Playhouses and festivals. Ballet and bands. Horticulture and history. Lectures and classes. Observatories and conservatories.

It's Easy and Economical to plan trips and vacations at 300 beautiful colleges and universities in 46 countries including 175 locations in the U.S. Many are open year 'round. MORT'S CAMPUS GUIDES tell you whom to contact for reservations, activities available on campus and nearby, rates, dates...all you need to know.

III

CONTENTS

V

CANADA

ATHENS COLLEGE
Athens, Alabama 35611

Athens is located in Tennessee Valley Authority dam
country, where Wheeler Lake and Guntersville Lake,
on the Tennessee River, are backed by dams that create
150 miles of lake frontage for aquatic vacationers.
Not far distant is Decatur, a hub for northern Alabama's
mountain/lake recreational pursuits. To the east of
Athens is Huntsville, and the George C. Marshall Space
Flight Center. The history of rocketry and space
exploration is unfolded here through exhibits and movies.

ACCOMMODATIONS
Single room—$3.00 per person per day
Double room—$5.00 per day
Baths are shared. Linens are $1.30 additional. Pets,
alcoholic beverages, and children under 18 years of
age are not permitted.
Accommodations are available to groups of 50 to 150
on a one-week basis.

MEALS (typical prices)
Breakfast — $ .85
Lunch — $1.37
Dinner — $1.58

ACTIVITIES (on campus or nearby)
Tennis, swimming, boating, fishing and aquatic sports.
Picnics, weekend trips and guided scenic tours. Exhibits
and movies at George C. Marshall Space Flight Center.

AVAILABLE DATES
June 2—August 8
Advance reservations are required.

CONTACT
Mr. S. C. Holmes
Business Manager
Telephone: (205) 232-1801, extension 204

LOMAX-HANNON JUNIOR COLLEGE
Greenville, Alabama 36037

Greenville is in south-central Alabama, about a half-hour from Montgomery which figured so importantly in the history of the Confederacy. Rural Alabama has many charms for tourists, typifying a comfortable, simple way of life. Natural wild areas are adjacent to the college campus, which itself includes 265 acres of wild timberland and swamp. Here vacationers can swim in a creek, instead of a pool. Nearby are beautiful hiking and camping areas to attract nature lovers.

ACCOMMODATIONS
Single room — $3.00 per person per day;
$21.00 per person per week
Double room — $3.00 per person per day;
$21.00 per person per week
Baths are shared. Alcoholic beverages not permitted.
Accommodations are available to students, alumni, adults, families and prospective matriculants.

MEALS
Restaurants and coffee shops are available in the area.

ACTIVITIES (on campus or nearby)
Swimming and camping. Picnic areas are available.
Camping equipment is available for rent.

AVAILABLE DATES
June 1 — September 1
Advance reservations are required.

CONTACT
Mr. Henry Cadenhead
Telephone: (205) 382-8511

UNIVERSITY OF SOUTH ALABAMA
Mobile, Alabama 36688

Mobile is a beautiful city, filled with magnificent antebellum houses decorated with iron grillwork balconies and superb gardens. The city is an interesting combination of French, Spanish and English influences reflecting its history of occupations prior to its seizure by the United States in 1813. The U.S.S. *Alabama* and the U.S.S. submarine, *Drum*, berthed at nearby Memorial Park may be boarded year 'round. Don't miss Oakleigh Mansion, a superlative pre-1850 plantation house which contains a fine collection of antiques and Mardi Gras memorabilia of past years. The Phoenix Museum, a restored firehouse, contains fire-fighting equipment dating from 1819, steam fire engines and memorabilia of Colonial Mobile. There is excellent swimming at the beaches on the Gulf Shore and Dauphin Island.

ACCOMMODATIONS
Single room — $4.50 per person per day
Double room — $2.50 per person per day
Baths are shared. Linens are provided. Pets are not permitted. Accommodations are available to students; alumni; prospective matriculants.

MEALS
A cafeteria and snack bar are located on campus.
A restaurant is near the campus. Typical prices are not available.

ACTIVITIES (on campus or nearby)
Golf — $1.00 per round; tennis is free; fresh and salt water fishing; swimming in season. Forts Gaines and Morgan, guarding the mouth of Mobile Bay, may be visited. Concerts, movies, drama and theatre companies in the city. New Orleans is two hours away.

AVAILABLE DATES
Year 'round.
Advance reservations are suggested.

CONTACT
Cecil Givens
Assistant Director of Housing
Department of Housing
307 University Boulevard
Telephone: (205) 460-6391

ALABAMA

TUSKEGEE INSTITUTE
Tuskegee, Alabama 36088

In 1813 Andrew Jackson began his campaign against
the Creek Indians from an old fort, located in the
Tuskegee, which had once been occupied by the French.
Booker T. Washington, a former slave, founded the
Institute in 1881. Some of the historical sights are the
Booker T. Washington Monument, the Oaks (Washington's
home), and the Carver Museum (which includes the work
of chemist George W. Carver, and displays of negro
contributions to our civilization and African art).
Montgomery, capital of Alabama, is about 40 miles away.
It overflows with the history of the Confederacy and has
many museums and restored mansions that are
fascinating to visit.

ACCOMMODATIONS
Single room — $5.30 per person per day; $95.00 monthly
Double room — $5.30 per person per day
Baths are private and shared. Linens and maid service are
provided. Pets and alcoholic beverages are not permitted.
$3.00 additional for an extra cot in the room.
Accommodations are available to the general public.

MEALS
Cafeteria (typical prices)
Meals are available in a food facility. There is a
snack bar on campus and restaurants are found in town.

ACTIVITIES (on campus or nearby)
Basketball, volleyball, shuffle board, gymnastic materials,
track, and athletic fields.

AVAILABLE DATES
Facilities are available year round. Reservations
are required.

CONTACT
T. W. Hardwich
c/o Residence Halls

UNIVERSITY OF ALASKA
College, Alaska 99701

A little less than 50 miles separates College from
Fairbanks, one of Alaska's major cities. In the middle
of the state, College is on the Tanana River which flows
into the Yukon. Beautiful scenery makes the area a
vacation delight, and a fine jumping-off point for
exploring Alaska during the mild summer season.

ACCOMMODATIONS
Single room — $11.00 per person per day;
$77.00 per person per week
Double room — $7.00 per person per day;
$49.00 per person per week
Apartment — $11.00 and up per person per day
Baths are shared. Linens and maid service are included.
Pets and firearms are not permitted.
Accommodations are available to students, alumni, adults,
families and prospective matriculants.

MEALS
Cafeteria (typical prices)
Breakfast — $2.25
Lunch — $2.75
Dinner — $3.50
A coffee shop is available.

ACTIVITIES (on campus or nearby)
Hiking and nature trails, mountain climbing, backpacking,
skiing and swimming. Area attractions are Alaskaland,
gold rush areas and gold dredging. Commercial tours may
be arranged and workshops on Alaska are available.

AVAILABLE DATES
May 20 — August 20
Advance reservations are preferred.

CONTACT
Dr. Harris Shelton
Student Housing Office
Telephone: (907) 479-7247

COCHISE COLLEGE
Douglas, Arizona 85607

Douglas vividly recalls the "Wild West." In the southeastern corner of the state just across the border from Agua Prieta, Mexico, Douglas is today a copper town in Cochise County scenically beautiful and rich in historical lore. Cowboys, miners, American and Mexican rustlers, smugglers and outlaws were the inhabitants of the region and it was sometimes referred to as "lawless Cochise County." Excursions in every direction from Douglas will reveal well-known historical names—Geronimo, Jack-the-Ripper, Cochise, Tombstone and Wyatt Earp. Some attractions are Bisbee Open-Pit Copper Mine; Tombstone, Arizona; Amerind Foundation—Museum of Indian Artifacts. Across the border is the quiet, pleasant Mexican town for shopping and night-life.

ACCOMMODATIONS
Single room—$5.00 per person per day;
$32.00 per person per week
Double room—$4.50 per person per day;
$28.50 per person per week
Baths are shared. There is no maid service.
Pets and alcoholic beverages are not permitted.
Accommodations are available to students, alumni, adults, families (special arrangement) and prospective matriculants.

MEALS
Cafeteria (typical prices)
Breakfast — $1.15;   Lunch — $1.25;   Dinner — $1.60
There is a snack bar on campus.
Steak night and special buffets—$1.90

ACTIVITIES (on campus or nearby)
Recreational facilities include tennis courts, swimming pool, astro-turf putting green, driving range, gymnasium and student union. There is no charge for swimming, fishing, tennis or hiking. Tennis, badminton, basketball, football, baseball, swimming, archery equipment are available for rent. Special events are Cochise County Fair (3 days, late September); Helldorado Days (3 days, mid-October).

AVAILABLE DATES
Available all year round. Advance reservations are required.

CONTACT
Mr. Donald Fry, Student Union
Telephone: (602) 364-3451, extension 204 and 288

PRESCOTT COLLEGE
Prescott, Arizona 86301

Located in the heart of Arizona, Prescott is a perfect
center point for the welcome visitor. In Prescott, be sure
to see the First Governor's Mansion, Sharlot Hall Museum
and the Smoki Museum. The 1,248,537 acre Prescott
National Forest should be seen for the breathtaking parts
of Sycamore Canyon, and Pine Mt. Primitive areas.
The Forest also provides picnicking, camping, hunting,
and fishing in the Granite Basin and Lynx Lakes.
Tombstone, "The Town Too Tough to Die" is only a few
hours south of Prescott. This city got its reputation
from the miners, gamblers, gunmen, and violence it
seemed to attract. The famous Earp-Clinton feud that
ended in a gunfight at the O.K. Corral was here. The Bird
Cage Theatre, O.K. Corral, and the Tombstone Courthouse
have been restored giving the town a "gun slinger" hier.
Take another day to go see the Grand Canyon, which is
truly a natural wonder of the world and must be seen
by anyone with the opportunity.

ACCOMMODATIONS
Single room — $8.00 per person per day
Suites accommodating up to 5 are available for $8.00
per person per day.
Baths are shared. Linen and maid service are provided.
No pets are allowed.
Accommodations are available to conference groups only.

MEALS
Meals are available on campus, prices vary according
to what is ordered. A cafeteria and snack bar are located
on campus. Restaurants are located off campus.

ACTIVITIES (on campus or nearby)
Swimming pool, baseball field, archery, field houses,
golf course.

AVAILABLE DATES
June 1 — August 15
Researvations must be made one year in advance.

CONTACT
Joseph Van Ecn Ecre
Director of Food Services and conventions

ARIZONA

ARIZONA STATE UNIVERSITY
Tempe, Arizona

Tempe is surrounded by three of Arizona's main cities:
Phoenix (the state capital), Mesa, Chandler. Tempe is a
small residential town that offers an escape from the
bustling cities that surround her. In Phoenix, where it is
said that the sun shines almost every day, there are a
great many things to see and do. The city parks have
swimming pools, tennis, fishing and boating. The Arizona
Mineral Museum with its rare collection of beautiful
gems, minerals, and ore samples is one of many museums
in Phoenix. The Desert Botanical Gardens, with 150
acres of plants from the world's deserts, should not be
missed. In Mesa, the old Mormon traditions are still
quite prevalent as demonstrated by its broad roads,
buildings, and gardens. The original Indian prehistoric
drainage ditches here are really interesting. And, don't
miss the Mormon Temple while in Mesa. Take another day
to visit the Williams Air Force Base in Chandler.

ACCOMMODATIONS
Single room—$10.00 per person per day; $70.00 weekly.
Double room—$3.50 per person per day; $24.50 weekly.
Baths are both shared and private. Linens are provided:
$1.50. Pets are not permitted.
Accommodations are available to students, alumni, and
prospective matriculants.

MEALS
Cafeteria (typical prices)
Breakfast — $ .60
Lunch — $1.35
Dinner — $1.85
Meals are available at a snack bar on campus.

ACTIVITIES (on campus or nearby)
Sightseeing: see description of area above.

AVAILABLE DATES
May 30—August 1
Reservations are required.

CONTACT
Russell S. Flaherty
Director of Housing, Memorial Union
Telephone: (602) 965-3515

HUMBOLT STATE UNIVERSITY
Arcata, California 95521

Located on the Humboldt Bay, Arcata is situated
approximately 2 miles from Eureka (named for that
famous cry, "Eureka! Gold!"). Legend has it that while
stationed at Fort Humboldt in Eureka, Ulysses S. Grant
was driven to drink by boredom and consequently resigned
his commission in 1854. Eureka is the home of Six Rivers
National Forest which has excellent fishing, hunting,
camping, and picnicking facilities. The country near the
city is beautiful — with deep forests of redwoods on the
one side, and the ocean on the other.

ACCOMMODATIONS
Two service plans (write for brochure).
Executive Service Plan:
Single room — $22.75 per person per day;
Double room — $20.75 per person per day
Basic Service Plan:
Single room — $14.00 per person per day;
Double room — $10.00 per person per day
Both plans include full room and board, linen and maid
services. Pets are not permitted.
Accommodations are available to conferences only.

MEALS
All meals are included in the daily rate.

ACTIVITIES (on campus or nearby)
Facilities available according to type of service plan used.

AVAILABLE DATES
Available during college summer break.
Advance reservations required.

CONTACT
Director of Conferences
Telephone: (707) 826-3368

PITZER COLLEGE
Claremont, California 91711

Claremont is one of the attractive suburban communities of the Los Angeles metropolitan area. It's 35 miles east of the metropolis, and 45 minutes to southern California's famed beaches, readily accessible to all of the area's attractions.

ACCOMMODATIONS
Single room — $6.00 per person per day;
$42.00 per person per week
Double room — $6.00 per person per day;
$42.00 per person per week
Additional charges may vary with the length of stay.
Children are not permitted.
Accommodations are available to students, alumni and adults. In order to preserve its tax exempt status as a non-profit educational institution, Pitzer College can only accommodate those groups whose travel coincides with, or is part of, an educational program. A statement outlining the educational purposes of the group is necessary.

MEALS
Cafeteria service is available by arrangement for groups of 75 or more.

ACTIVITIES (on campus or nearby)
Nearby southern California attractions.

AVAILABLE DATES
June 15 — September 15
Advance reservations are required.

CONTACT
Mrs. Vicke Selk
Scott Hall
1150 Mills Avenue
Telephone: (714) 626-8511, extension 2643

UNIVERSITY OF CALIFORNIA — BERKELEY
(International House)
Berkeley, California 94720

Berkeley is directly opposite the Golden Gate, and right across the bay from San Francisco, which flavors the city with a rich urban and multi-cultural influence. Because the average monthly temperature rarely exceeds 65°F, Berkeley has been called one of the nation's most refreshing cities. All around and within the San Francisco Bay are are relics of towns once inhabited by rough and tough transients eager for gold. Especially fascinating are the Chinese Camp; Fiddletown, whose inhabitants were said to always be fiddling; Drytown which once had 26 saloons and a wild reputation; Sierra City, once the home of the Order of E Clampus Vitus, known for its ingenious hoaxes, practical jokes and hilarious initiation rites (the new member would sometimes find himself in a state of semi-conscious confusion). While in San Francisco, be sure to stop in at Ripley's Believe It or Not Museum, filled with over 2,000 oddities. Shop in the exclusive stores and shops in Ghiardelli Square, Cow Hollow, and Union Square. San Francisco has some of the finest restaurants in the world — you can take a gourmet trip around the world without leaving the city.

ACCOMMODATIONS
Single room — $55.00 per person per week
Double room — $45.00 per person per week
Rates include full room and board.
Baths are shared, and linens are provided. Pets are not permitted.
Accommodations are available to students, scholars, researchers, and educationally oriented groups.

MEALS
All three meals are served in a food facility in International House, and are included in the fee.

ACTIVITIES (on campus or nearby)
Ping pong, badminton, music and practice rooms, stereo listening rooms, library, dances, folk dancing weekly, excellent hiking around campus and in Merinde County.

AVAILABLE DATES
late June — early September
Advance reservations are required.

CONTACT
Residence Officer, International House
2299 Piedmont Ave.
Telephone: (415) 642-9470

CALIFORNIA

CALIFORNIA STATE UNIVERSITY
Fresno, California 93710

Guild Winery, one of America's largest, and the world's
largest dried fruit packing plant, Sun-Maid, are in
Fresno, in the heart of the San Joaquin Valley where
the weather is warm and dry and the air is clear. Don't
miss the Underground Gardens, a remarkable 5 acre
underground construction, built by one man over a period
of 40 years, which contains grottos, gardens and 65 rooms.
The Sequoia and Kings Canyon National Parks are 54
miles east of Fresno. The city's Museum of Natural
History and Junion Museum contains live animals,
dioramic habitats, an aquarium and the Yokuts Indian
Room. The fruit processing plant may be toured from
Monday to Friday, except holidays. Just 21 miles north
is the Millerton Lake State Recreation Area which
provides riding, picnicking, water skiing, fishing,
boating and swimming.

ACCOMMODATIONS
Single room — $7.00 per person per day; $49.00 weekly
Double room — $6.00 per person per day; $42.00 weekly
Suite (accommodating 6) — $7.00 per person per day;
$49.00 weekly
Baths are shared. Linens are included in the fee.
Pets are not permitted.
Accommodations are available to students, alumni,
prospective matriculants and educationally related
individuals and groups.

MEALS
Prices are not available. There is a snack bar and
restaurant on campus.

ACTIVITIES (on campus or nearby)
On campus: swimming, tennis. Off campus: golf, fishing,
hiking. The Pacific Ocean is within driving distance.
There are 12 golf courses in the area. Guided tours of the
area are available. There are many local wineries which
provide tours of their facilities.

AVAILABLE DATES
June 8 — September 1
Reservations are suggested.

CONTACT
Edward Mastropoalo
Director of Residence Halls
Cedar & Shaw
Telephone: (209) 487-2028

FRESNO STATE COLLEGE
Fresno, California

Fresno is located in the great central area of California known as the "Garden of the Sun". Fresno is a bustling city filled with things to do. Go to Roeding Park, 157 acres that are known for a variety of trees and shrubs both tropical and arctic. Other interesting sights are; the Underground Gardens, a maze of 65 rooms, gardens, and grottos that cover five acres constructed by one man in a period of about 40 years; The Yosemite National Park; Fresno Museum of Natural History and Jr. Museum with an aquarium, telescope viewing, and live animal dioramas, and if skiing is your sport, be sure to go to the China Peak area in Sierra National Forest.

ACCOMMODATIONS
Single room — $6.50 per person daily
Double room — $5.50 per person daily
Suites accommodating 6 are available for $6.00 per person daily.
Baths are shared. Linen service is prvoided. Maid service is provided for $.50. Pets are not permitted.
Accommodations are available to families and groups.

MEALS
Cafeteria (typical prices)
Breakfast — $1.35
Lunch — $1.50
Dinner — $2.00
There is a snack bar on campus.

ACTIVITIES (on campus or nearby)
Tennis courts, swimming pool w/arrangements, and a gymnasium.

AVAILABLE DATES
June 16 — August

CONTACT
Gail Griego, Conference Director
Telephone: (209) 487-1001

PACIFIC COLLEGE
Fresno, California 93702

In the heart of central California's San Joaquin Valley—
The "Garden of the Sun"—Fresno offers numerous
attractions to vacationers. Besides its traffic-free downtown shopping mall, there are guided tours of the huge
local fruit drying plant, and one of the nation's largest
wineries. Local attractions include Roeding Park, featuring
trees and shrubs ranging from arctic to tropical, and the
grottos and maze of the Underground Gardens. For
outdoor interests, the Millerton Lake State Recreational
Area, the snow-capped mountains of Sierra National
Forest and the Yosemite, Sequoia and Kings Canyon
National Parks are all nearby.

ACCOMMODATIONS
Single room—$3.00 per person per day
Double room—$3.00 per person per day
Pets, smoking and alcoholic beverages are not permitted.
Accommodations are available to students, alumni, adults,
families and prospective matriculants.

MEALS
Cafeteria (typical prices)
Breakfast — $1.25
Lunch — $2.00
Dinner — $1.75

ACTIVITIES (on campus or nearby)
Ping pong, pool, basketball, tennis and volleyball.
Basketball, tennis and volleyball equipment is available
for rent.

AVAILABLE DATES
June 15—Sept. 1
Advance reservations are required.

CONTACT
Summer Conference Coordinator
1717 South Chestnut Street
Telephone: (209) 251-7194

NORTHROP INSTITUTE OF TECHNOLOGY
Inglewood, California 92601

Every attraction that brings visitors to the Los Angeles area is readily accessible from Inglewood. This city is the home of Hollywood Park Race Track and near Los Angeles International Airport. Well-known vacation lures include Disneyland and the mountains, ocean beaches and desert areas of southern California. Besides the sunny climate, there are countless things to see and do in the area. A 500-mile tour of historic missions. A mountain and desert tour for the adventurous. History-filled parks and museums. Magnificent gardens. Marineland. Fossils in the La Brea Tar Pits. And miles and miles of ocean beaches.

ACCOMMODATIONS
Single room—$5.50 per person per day;
$38.50 per person per week
Double room—$4.50 per person per day;
$31.50 per person per week
Baths are shared. Pets and children under 16 years
of age are not permitted.
Accommodations are available to students, alumni, adults, families and prospective matriculants.

MEALS
Cafeteria (typical prices)
Breakfast — $1.30
Lunch — $1.60
Dinner — $2.15

ACTIVITIES
Nearby Southern California attractions.

AVAILABLE DATES
Facilities are available all year round.
Advance reservations are required.

CONTACT
Robert P. Olson
P.O. Box 900
733 S. Hindry
Inglewood, California 90306
Telephone: (213) 641-5788

LA VERNE COLLEGE
La Verne, California 91750

All the attractions of the Los Angeles area are readily accessible from La Verne, a quiet town 40 minutes from the southern California metropolis. Beaches are an hour away, the mountains and Pomona Valley a half hour's drive.

ACCOMMODATIONS
Single room — $5.00 per person per day;
$35.00 per person per week
Double room — $4.00 per person per day;
$28.00 per person per week
Baths are shared. Children must be supervised.
Pets and alcoholic beverages are not permitted.
Accommodations are available to students, alumni, adults, families and prospective matriculants.

MEALS
Restaurants and coffee shop are in the area.

ACTIVITIES (on campus or nearby)
Nearby public facilities.

AVAILABLE DATES
June 10 — August 30
Reservations are required one to two weeks in advance.

CONTACT
Miss Rena Bever
1950 Third Street
Telephone: (714) 593-3511, extension 205

COLLEGE OF THE HOLY NAME
Oakland, California 94619

San Francisco is just across the bay, Berkeley is next
door, so that Oakland is right in the center of all the
metropolitan hub-bub of one of the most famous and
well-loved areas in the world. A 20-minute ride on the
new Rapid Transit system will bring you into the center
of San Francisco—a city you will lose your heart to.
There are so many interesting places to go, things to eat,
buy, and see, and people to meet in San Francisco that it's
impossible to experience them all in a short period of
time. While in the city, you can be assured of a bright,
lively, and exciting night life—visit "Top o' the Mark,"
one of the most famous cocktail lounges in the world,
offering a fine view of the city. The theatres are known
for their long successful seasons; the restaurants are
numbered amongst the finest in the world; the stores
and shops are ranked with the most exclusive—in short,
San Francisco has it all, an atmosphere at once warm and
familiar, and yet totally unique and exotic.

ACCOMMODATIONS
Single room—$9.00 per person per day;
$11.50 per person per day with meals
Double room—$7.50 per person per day;
$10.00 per person per day with meals.
Suite (accommodates 2 people) —$15.00 per person per day
Suites include private bath, other bath faciilties are
shared. Linens are provided. Pets and alcoholic beverages
are not permitted.
Accommodations are available to groups, students,
alumni, adults, families, small children, and prospective
matriculants.

MEALS
Cafeteria (typical prices)
Breakfast — $1.00
Lunch — $1.25
Dinner — $2.00

ACTIVITIES (on campus or nearby)
Swimming, hiking, tennis courts.

AVAILABLE DATES
Year round. Advance reservations are required.

CONTACT
Director of Residence
3500 Mountain Blvd.
Telephone: (415) 436-1287 & 1292

LOMA LINDA UNIVERSITY
Riverside, California 92505

There's a freeway to Riverside from the thickly clustered communities of the Los Angeles metropolitan area. It whisks travelers through vast navel orange groves to the city known as the "Center of the Orange Empire." A point of interest in town is the Parent Washington Navel Orange Tree, which was propagated from one of the original trees from Bahia, Brazil, where the navel orange mutation was discovered. The mission influence is seen everywhere. In the Mission Inn. In Mount Rubidoux Memorial Park—reputedly once the altar of the sun worshippers, now topped by a cross in memory of Fray Junipero Serra, founder of the California missions. For auto racing buffs, Riverside International Raceway is a year-round attraction.

ACCOMMODATIONS
Single room—$4.00 per person first day;
$2.50 per person each succeeding day
Double room—$3.50 per person first day;
$2.50 per person each succeeding day
Pets, smoking and alcoholic beverages are not permitted.
Accommodations are available to students, alumni, adults, families and prospective matriculants.

MEALS
Cafeteria (typical prices)
Breakfast — $1.35
Lunch — $1.65
Dinner — $1.55

ACTIVITIES (on campus or nearby)
Swimming, handball, tennis and horseback riding.
Southern California attractions.

AVAILABLE DATES
June 20—August 15
Advance reservations are required.

CONTACT
Miss Tracy R. Teele
Telephone: (714) 785-2100

CALIFORNIA STATE UNIVERSITY
Sacramento, California 95825

For floriculture fans and hobbyists, Sacramento is both the picturesque state capital and the "Camellia Capital of the World." The city is steeped in California history. Captain John A. Sutter's original settlement. The entrance to the gold rush country. Western terminal of the Pony Express, and later, home of the financiers of the Central Pacific Railroad, which first crossed the Sierras. A replica of the Golden Gate Bridge serves as a footbridge across the American River on the university campus. In late summer, there's the California State Fair, and adult and junior concerts in William Land Park. For sightseeing, San Francisco and Lake Tahoe are nearby.

ACCOMMODATIONS
Single room — $5.00 per person per day;
$35.00 per person per week
Double room — $4.00 per person per day;
$28.00 per person per week
Pets are not permitted.
Accommodations are available to students, alumni and prospective matriculants.

MEALS
A cafeteria is available.

ACTIVITIES (on campus or nearby)
Basketball, tennis, bicycling, fishing and swimming. There is a nominal fee for swimming.

AVAILABLE DATES
July 1 — August 30
Advance reservations are not required.

CONTACT
Dr. John M. Heath
6000 J Street
Telephone: (916) 454-6496

LONE MOUNTAIN COLLEGE
San Francisco, California 94118

San Francisco offers such a myriad of sights, activities, museums, cultural events, and natural beauty that only a visit can do it justice. Chinese New Year in San Francisco has been long known as the largest and most exciting Chinese festival in the U.S.—a week of Chinese street dancing, parades, carnival, cultural exhibits and the Golden Dragon display. The Golden Gate Park dramatizes San Francisco's beauty in 1,017 acres featuring several thousand different varieties of shrubs and plants.

ACCOMMODATIONS
Single room—$15.00 per person per day
(non-student rate—room and board)
Double room—$12.50 per person per day
(non-student rate—room and board)
Single room—$12.50 per person per day
(student rate—room and board)
$5.00 per person per day (student rate—room only)
Double room—$10.00 per person per day
(student rate—room and board)
$5.00 per person per day (student rate—room only)
Special rates are possible for extended periods. Group rates are available for both lodging and meals.
Baths are shared and private. Linens are included.
Pets are not permitted.
Accommodations are available to students, alumni, adults, families and prospective matriculants.

MEALS
Cafeteria (typical prices)
Breakfast — $1.10
Lunch — $1.50
Dinner — $1.85
Meals are also available a la carte.

ACTIVITIES (on campus or nearby)
Tennis, day care center, swimming, hiking and boating.

AVAILABLE DATES
June 2—August 26
December 26—January 25
Advance reservations are required.

CONTACT
Susan L. Brissenden, Director of Housing
2800 Turk Boulevard
Telephone: (415) 752-7000, extension 282

SAN FRANCISCO STATE UNIVERSITY
San Francisco, California 94132

San Francisco offers such a myriad of sights, activities, museums, cultural events, and natural beauty that only a visit can do it justice. Chinese New Year in San Francisco has been long known as the largest and most exciting Chinese festival in the U.S. — a week of Chinese street dancing, parades, carnival, cultural exhibits and the Golden Dragon display. The Golden Gate Park dramatizes San Francisco's beauty in 1,017 acres featuring several thousand different varieties of shrubs and plants and the McLaurel Rhododendron Dell. The famed cable cars provide a unique opportunity to view the city from its hills and enjoy a memorable ride. To briefly list but a few other attractions: Fisherman's Wharf, Ghirardelli Square, Golden Gate Bridge, Lake Merced, Union Square, The Embarcadero, San Francisco-Oakland Bay Bridge, Civic Center, and the San Francisco Zoological Gardens.

ACCOMMODATIONS
Single room — $8.00 per person per day;
$58.50 per person per week (room and board)
Double room — $5.00 per person per day;
$43.50 per person per week (room and board)
Baths are shared. Linens are included. Pets and children under 14 years of age are not permitted.
Accommodations are available to students and student-related groups only.

MEALS
Cafeteria (typical prices)
Breakfast — $1.25
Lunch — $2.00
Dinner — $2.50

ACTIVITIES (on campus or nearby)
All kinds of guided tours, tennis, swimming, sports, folk dancing and card games. Athletic and game equipment is available.

AVAILABLE DATES
June 6 — August 25
September 10 — May 30 (limited facilities)
Advance reservations are required.

CONTACT
Verducci Hall
770 Lake Merced Boulevard
Telephone: (415) 469-2476

CALIFORNIA

SAN JOSE STATE COLLEGE
San Jose, California 95112

San Jose, on the south end of the San Francisco Bay, 50 miles from San Francisco, is a quaint little city of blue skies and lovely California climate. Ever since Dione Warwick immortalized San Jose in her song "Do You Know the Way to San Jose?", the city has been deluged with tourists. There are many fascinating points of interest such as: the Mystery House, with 160 rooms, thousands of windows, blank walls, trap doors, blind chimneys, secret passageways; the Egyptian Museum, which houses one of the most comprehensive collections of Egyptian and Oriental antiquities in the nation, including the Benediction Stone, under which Moses stood as he appealed to God on behalf of the people of Israel. Be sure to see the Japanese Friendship Garden patterned after the famous and lovely Korakuen Park in Okayama, Japan.

ACCOMMODATIONS
Single room — $7.00 per person per day
Double room — $4.00 per person per day
Suite (accommodates up to 8 people) — $4.00 per person per day.
Baths are private in the suites, otherwise they are shared. Linens and maid services are provided. Pets are not permitted.
Accommodations are available to conferences, workshops, groups with educationally related activities.

MEALS
Cafeteria (typical prices)
Breakfast, lunch, and dinner are served in a cafeteria on campus for a total of $5 - $6 per person per day.

ACTIVITIES (on campus or nearby)
On campus there are archery fields, athletic fields, and gymnasium facilities.

AVAILABLE DATES
June 15 — August 15
Reservations are suggested.

CONTACT
Ms. Evelyn Robinson
Assistant Housing Director
125 South Seventh Street
Telephone: (408) 277-2126

CALIFORNIA LUTHERAN COLLEGE
Thousand Oaks, California 91360

Thousand Oaks is located on the Ventura Freeway
(U.S. 101), an hours drive from Los Angeles, one of the
nation's largest cities with abundant cultural, recreational
and social opportunities. Thousand Oaks is bounded on
the west by the rich agricultural area of the Oxnard
Plains. Ten miles to the north begin the slopes of the
rugged Topatopa Mountain Range. Northeast is the
Mojave Desert, and 18 miles south over the Santa Monica
Mountains are the Pacific Ocean beaches of Malibu
and Zuma.

ACCOMMODATIONS
$8.50 per adult per day (room and board)
$7.50 per child per day (room and board)
Pets and alcoholic beverages are not permitted.
Accommodations are available to students, alumni, adults,
families and prospective matriculants.

MEALS
Cafeteria (typical prices)
Breakfast — $1.25
Lunch — $1.75
Dinner — $2.00
A coffee shop is available.

ACTIVITIES (on campus or nearby)
Swimming, golf and horseback riding.

AVAILABLE DATES
Due to the demand for our facilities, we are occupied
for the summer 1974.

CONTACT
Mr. Donald Garrison
Summer Program Director
60 Olsen Road
Telephone: (805) 492-2411, extensions 287, 288, 289

LORETTO HEIGHTS COLLEGE
Denver, Colorado 80236

Denver's rapid growth to the capital city of Colorado started with the early United States gold and silver rush. A saloon, cabins and the trappings of early westernization characterized the main street, and the town became rapidly populated to city proportions. The South Platte River, Great Plains, foothills of the Rocky Mountains, the dry and mild climate, and high altitude make Denver a desirable vacation, cultural, commercial and industrial metropolis.

ACCOMMODATIONS
Single room — $14.00 per person per day
(includes three meals)
Double room — $10.00 per person per day
(includes three meals)
Pets, children under 18 years of age, and alcoholic beverages are not permitted.
Accommodations are available to students only.

MEALS
There is no set cost for meals. A cafeteria is available on campus.

ACTIVITIES (on campus or nearby)
Tennis, skiing and mountain climbing. Six-week creative arts program in June and July.

AVAILABLE DATES
June 15 — August 15
Advance reservations are required.

CONTACT
Mr. Francis J. Kelly
Vice President for Administrative Operations
3001 South Federal Boulevard
Telephone: (303) 922-4116

REGIS COLLEGE
Denver, Colorado 80221

Regis College offers all the cultural and scenic
attractions of Denver. The "Mile High City," Colorado's
capital, is noted for its dry, mild climate. To the east
are the Great Plains; to the west, the foothills and
front range of the Rocky Mountains. There are 150
parks within the city, many with unique attractions.
Nearby is the Denver Mountain Park System, extending
45 miles to Summit Lake. The Denver Symphony is
nationally known, as are the art museum and public
library. Tours are available at the United States Mint.
Other "must see" sites are Larimer Square, restoration of
Denver's first street, the Space Walk on the Security
Life Building, Forney's Transportation Museum, and the
dioramas and exhibits of the Mesa Verde and the
Old West at the Colorado State Museum.

ACCOMMODATIONS
Single room — add $3.00 per person per day to charges
stated below
Double room or suite — under 50 people:
$15.00 per person per day; $105.00 per person per week
50-99 people:
$14.00 per person per day; $98.00 per person per week
100 people:
$13.00 per person per day; $91.00 per person per week
Baths are shared. Linens are $1.00 additional. Pets and
unaccompanied children are not permitted.
Accommodations are available for conferences and
group meetings only.

MEALS Cafeteria (typical prices)
Breakfast — $ .75
Lunch — $1.15
Dinner — $1.75
A coffee shop available.

ACTIVITIES (on campus or nearby)
Swimming, handball and tennis. There is a 50¢ fee
per person for swimming.

AVAILABLE DATES
June 10 — August 1
Advance reservations are required.

CONTACT
Miss Lynne Hansen
Scheduling Office, Student Center
West 50 Street and Lowell Boulevard
Telephone: (303) 433-8471

COLORADO MOUNTAIN COLLEGE
Glenwood Springs, Colorado 81601

Glenwood Springs is another of Colorado's famed
vacation havens. At the junction of the Roaring Fork
and Colorado Rivers on U.S. Highway 6, it's an excellent
area for a wealth of outdoor activities. To the east is
the internationally acclaimed year-round resort of Vail.
To the south, Snowmass, the summer music festival and
cultural attractions at Aspen. And to the west, Rifle,
the sleeping giant of shale oil activity. The lofty region
unfolds countless vistas of incomparable beauty, trout-
filled lakes and streams, and excellent game and
hiking country.

ACCOMMODATIONS
Single room—$20.00 per day;
$75.00 per person per week
Double room—$25.00 per day;
$47.50 per person per week
Baths are private. Pets are not permitted.
Accommodations are available to students, alumni, adults,
families and prospective matriculants.

MEALS
Cafeteria (typical prices)
Breakfast — $1.05
Lunch — $1.35
Dinner — $1.60

ACTIVITIES (on campus or nearby)
Swimming, hiking, tennis and fishing (no fees). Activity
programs include tours, backpack trips and horseback
riding (must be arranged in advance). Some of the area's
scenic, recreational, historic and cultural attractions
include Glenwood Canyon, Hanging Lake and Park,
Sweetwater Creek and Lake, Noname Creek and hiking
area, Redstone, Marble and Sunlight ski areas, Aspen,
Snowmass, Hot Springs Pool and Doc Holiday's grave.

AVAILABLE DATES
June 1—August 31
Advance reservations are required.

CONTACT
Manager
Pinon Alps Apartments
Telephone: (303) 945-8102

U.S. INTERNATIONAL UNIVERSITY
Colorado Alpine Campus
Steamboat Springs, Colorado 80477

Rivers and mountains of powdery, glistening snow outline the valley where Steamboat Springs earned its fame as the home of five world ski-jumping records. For ski aficionados, the Rocky Mountains provide one of the best, if not the best, ski areas in the U.S. Elk herds, medicinal springs and the Routt National Forest enhance its bucolic ambiance.

ACCOMMODATIONS
Single and double rooms—
Nov. 28 - Dec. 22: $10.00 per person per day
Dec. 23 - Jan. 5: $14.00 per person per day
Jan. 6 - Easter: $12.00 per person per day
Above rates include full breakfast and full dinner.
Single and double rooms—Post-Easter - Nov. 27: $7.00 per person per day (room only) ; $12.00 per person per day (full breakfast and dinner).
Baths are shared. Linens and maid service are included in the fee. Pets and alcoholic beverages are not permitted. Accommodations are available to: general public. Facility is also an American Youth Hostel. Group rates are available: inquire directly.

MEALS
For residents not using the meal plan (see above)
Cafeteria (typical prices)
Breakfast — $1.50
Lunch — $2.00
Dinner — $3.50

ACTIVITIES (on campus or nearby)
Camping, white water rafting, skiing, hiking, fishing, tennis, horseback riding, hunting, and kayaking.

AVAILABLE DATES
The college facilities are available all year round.
Advance reservations are suggested.
Skiing season is Dec. 5—April 15.

CONTACT
Mr. Richard Carlson
Property Manager
U.S.I.U., Box 968
Telephone: 879-4176/0590 (day)
          879-2136 (night)

UNIVERSITY OF NEW HAVEN
West Haven, Connecticut 06516

Only 78 miles from New York City, New Haven combines
the ambiance of a university town with the traditional life
of New England. Long Island Sound, New Haven Harbor
and Quinnipiac River border the city, providing its environs with a myriad of summer and winter water sports.
Yale Art Gallery and Peabody Museum are two of several
museums and cultural landmarks in New Haven. The
Sterling Memorial and Beinecke Rare Book and Manu-
script Libraries draw scholars from all over the world.

ACCOMMODATIONS
Single room — $7.00 per person per day;
$45.00 per person per week
Double room — $5.00 per person per day;
$30 per person per week
Baths are shared. Pets are not permitted.
Accommodations are available to students, adults and
prospective matriculants.

MEALS
Cafeteria (typical prices)
Breakfast — $ .80 to $1.00
Lunch — $1.00 to $1.25
Dinner — area restaurant

ACTIVITIES (on campus or nearby)
Three concert series and a stock theatre are offered
during the summer.

AVAILABLE DATES
June 15 — August 15
Advance reservations are required.

CONTACT
Mr. Philip S. Robertson
Director of Housing and Student Center
300 Orange Avenue
Telephone: (203) 934-6321, extension 378 or 383

MARYMOUNT COLLEGE
Boca Raton, Florida 33432

Boca Raton is a resort town and a suburban area located on Florida's eastern "Gold Coast." It is 40 miles north of Miami and 25 miles from the Fort Lauderdale and Palm Beach airports. Recreational activities include swimming, tennis, golf, surf-casting and deep sea fishing. There are two public beaches and six superior golf courses nearby. Cultural and recreational activities are numerous.

ACCOMMODATIONS
Double room — $10.00 per person per day;
$65.00 per person per week
Accommodations are available to students, alumni, adults, families, prospective matriculants and groups.

MEALS
Cafeteria (typical prices)
Breakfast — $1.00
Lunch — $1.25
Dinner — $1.50

ACTIVITIES (on campus or nearby)
Swimming, fishing, tennis, golf and boating.

AVAILABLE DATES
May 20 — September 1
December 20 — February 1
Advance reservations are required.

CONTACT
Director of Conferences
Telephone: (305 395-4301

FLORIDA INSTITUTE OF TECHNOLOGY
Melbourne, Florida 32901

Just south of our country's first space ports at Cape
Kennedy and the Patrick Air Force Base, Melbourne is
on the Intracoastal Waterway and a center for all aquatic
recreational activities. Just across the Indian River (you
can fish from its causeways) are Melbourne Beach,
Indialantic, Indian Harbor Beach and Satellite Beach —
all on the Atlantic Ocean. A half dozen parks offer a
wide range of recreational facilities. For sightseeing,
Disney World, the Kennedy Space Center, Cypress
Gardens, Marineland, Silver Springs, Tropical Gardens
and St. Augustine, the oldest city in the United States,
are all nearby. On the campus is the Dent Smith Trail,
a botanical garden featuring 200 species of palm.

ACCOMMODATIONS
Single room — $5.50 per person per day;
$38.50 per person per week
Double room — $4.00 per person per day;
$28.00 per person per week
Special reduced rates are available for stays of 6 days
or more and for family and other groups.
Special rates also available to several local attractions.
Write for brochure.
Baths are shared or, for $1.00 per person additional,
a private bath is available. Pets are not permitted.
Accommodations are available to students, alumni, adults,
families and prospective matriculants.

MEALS
A cafeteria and coffee shop are available.

ACTIVITIES (on campus or nearby)
Races, jai alai, aquatic sports such as swimming, surfing,
sailing, fishing, as well as tennis, golf and bowling. There
is an additional charge for sailboats and scuba equipment.

AVAILABLE DATES
June 10 — August 31
Advance reservations are required.

CONTACT
F. I. T. Vacation Center
P.O. Box 1150
Telephone: (305) 723-3701

BOISE STATE COLLEGE
Boise, Idaho

Boise is the capital and largest city of Idaho. There are
many wooded areas scattered throughout the city along
with many nearby parks, which offer boating, fishing,
swimming and picnicking. Some of these are: the Julia
Davis Park which houses the Idaho State Historical
Society Museum and the Boise Gallery of Art; Ann
Morrison Memorial Park with its beautiful formal
gardens; Lucky Peak State Park; and Boise National
Park with its abandoned mines and ghost towns. About
40 miles away is Idaho City, which during the gold rush
almost became the capital city of the state. Be sure
not to miss the mining camp ruins located here.

ACCOMMODATIONS
Single room — $4.50 per person per day
Double room — $3.50 per person per day
Suits accommodate 10 to 25, rates depend upon services
provided. Baths are shared. Linens and maid service
are provided.
Accommodations are available to students, prospective
matriculants and conference groups.

MEALS
All meals are available in the campus cafeteria,
prices vary according to what is ordered.

ACTIVITIES (on campus or nearby)
Fishing, boating, swimming, golf, tennis, backpacking.
Each dormitory has a recreation room.

AVAILABLE DATES
June 1 — August 15
Reservations are required.

CONTACT
Mr. J. Vestal, Director
1910 College Blvd.
Telephone: (208) 385-1011

AURORA COLLEGE
Aurora, Illinois 60507

Aurora, like many a river community, developed as two towns on either side of the Fox River. Rivalry at one time was intense. In fact, after the merger of the left and right bank towns into one, there were fierce verbal battles over the location of public buildings. A solution was found by erecting a Civic Center on one of the many islands that lie between the two banks. Although near Chicago, Aurora has an industry and economy of its own, yet is close enough to the Windy City to enjoy its many attractions.

ACCOMMODATIONS
Double room — $6.50 per person per day
Baths are shared. Linens are included. There is a nominal charge for maid service. Pets, smoking, and alcoholic beverages are not permitted.
Accommodations are available to students, alumni, adults, families and prospective matriculants.

MEALS
Cafeteria (typical prices)
Breakfast — $1.50
Lunch — $1.75
Dinner — $2.75
Group rates available upon request.

ACTIVITIES (on campus or nearby)
Swimming, fishing, tennis, hiking, etc. There is a nominal fee for tennis.

AVAILABLE DATES
June 10 — August 10
Advance reservations are required.

CONTACT
Miss Evelyn Swenson
Business Assistant
347 South Gladstone Avenue
Telephone: (312) 892-6431

EASTERN ILLINOIS UNIVERSITY
Charleston, Illinois 61920

Abraham Lincoln practiced law in Charleston and there's
a collection of his memorabilia at the Coles County
Courthouse here. Nine miles south of the city is the
Lincoln Log Cabin, a reconstruction on the original
foundations, which was built by Abraham's father in
 837. Lincoln's parents are buried nearby in Shiloh
Cemetery. Lincoln left Charleston to become President
and ate his last meal here at his stepmother's house,
the Moore Home. The fourth of the famous Lincoln-
Douglas debates took place in the city and a collection
of materials relating to the historic encounters are housed
in the Debate House. The University itself contains the
Paul Sargent Art Gallery. There's picnicking, fishing,
swimming and boating at a nearby park and lake.

ACCOMMODATIONS
Single room — $7.50 per person per day
Double room — $5.00 per person per day
Pets are not permitted. Baths are shared. Linens are
provided.
Accommodations are available to conference groups.

MEALS
Cafeteria (typical prices)
Breakfast — $1.00
Lunch — $1.50
Dinner — $2.00

ACTIVITIES (on campus or nearby)
Gymnasium on campus; Paul Sargent Art Gallery.
Fishing and picnicking at Fox Ridge State Park;
swimming, boating, etc. at Lake Charleston. Coles County
Fair: late July-early August (1 week). Recreational
equipment is included in the fee.

AVAILABLE DATES
May 20 — August 15
Reservations are required.

CONTACT
Mr. Honckon, Assoc. Dean of Housing
or, Mr. Lindburgh, Director of Arrangements
Telephone: (217) 581-3923

ROOSEVELT UNIVERSITY
Chicago, Illinois 60605

Chicago is a fascinating city—it lies along the shore of Lake Michigan, hence the name of "Windy City." There is an inexhaustible supply of cultural events and places to see. Don't miss: Grant Park which includes the Field Museum of Natural History, one of the largest natural history museums with famous collections of primitive art; the John G. Shedd Aquarium; the Adler Planetarium; the Art Institute of Chicago with well-known collections of sculpture, paintings, Oriental art, and primitive art. Be sure to stop in Chinatown and enjoy the foods and the people. Old Town, one of the most exotic parts of Chicago, extends for a half mile down N. Wells St. Here, you find yourself on a bright, colorful street filled with all sorts of book stores, art galleries, antique and curio shops tucked in nooks and crannies, restaurants, and nightclubs. Chicago is famous for its excellent shopping facilities, restaurants to suit any palate, entertainment from pubs to discotheques and nightclubs to the opera and theatre.

ACCOMMODATIONS
Double room—$40.00 per person per week
Baths are shared. Linens are provided. Pets are not allowed. All residents must be currently attending school or be in a co-op program or internship.

MEALS
All meals are included in cost of room and board. There is a cafeteria and a snack bar on campus, and many restaurants off-campus.

ACTIVITIES (on campus or nearby)
Free game room, discount tickets to shows, theatres, and museums.

AVAILABLE DATES
Facilities are available all year round. Reservations are required.

CONTACT
Mr. Larry Lund
Director of Herman Crown Center
425 South Wabash Ave.
Telephone: (312) 341-2004

BARAT COLLEGE
Lake Forest, Illinois 60045

Lake Forest is just 15 minutes from Lake Michigan, and 30 miles from Chicago. The lake is particularly beautiful during the summer months and offers swimming, boating and fishing facilities. Chicago, the second most populous city in the U.S., has something for everyone. The city has 14 legitimate theatres, fine stores rivaling New York's Fifth Avenue, fascinating and diverse museums, hundreds of parks, and a restaurant to cater to any palate. Don't miss: Marshall Field & Co., one of the most famous stores in the world with a Tiffany dome made of over one million pieces of glass; go to "Bughouse Square" (Washington Square), which was given to the city with the condition that free speech never be prohibited within its boundaries. Visit Lincoln Park, the largest in Chicago, which includes the Lincoln Park Zoological Gardens, Lincoln Park Conservatory, Chicago Academy of Sciences, and the Chicago Historical Society.

ACCOMMODATIONS
Double room — $6.00 per person per day
Baths are shared. Linens are provided. No pets are permitted.
Accommodations are available to groups and conferences.

MEALS
Cafeteria (typical prices)
Breakfast — rates not available
Lunch — rates not available
Dinner — rates not available
Conference rate of $11.00 per person per day
for complete room and board.

ACTIVITIES (on campus or nearby)
Gymnasium available at no fee on campus.

AVAILABLE DATES
June — mid-August
Advance reservations are required.

CONTACT
Sister Hopkins
Director of Housing
Telephone: (312) 234-3000

WESTERN ILLINOIS UNIVERSITY
Macomb, Illinois 61455

Macomb, named for General Alexander Macomb of
War of 1812 fame, is notable for having two lovely
public squares. It contains a well-known pottery which
may be toured. Two nearby parks provide facilities for
fishing, boating and picnicking. Galesburg, less than an
hour's drive north, is Carl Sandburg's birthplace.
Many of the famous poet's possessions are on display
here, in a three-room cottage which also contains relics
associated with Abraham Lincoln. Fourteen miles further
north is Bishop Hill, a former Swedish immigrant
commune. It is still occupied by descendants of the
original settlers. Of the thirteen buildings still extant,
don't miss: Colony Church, containing Olof Kans'
paintings, and Steeple Building, a Greek Revival
structure with an extraordinary one-handed clock and
historical memorabilia.

ACCOMMODATIONS
Single room — $8.00 per person per day;
$38.50 per person per week
Double room — $6.00 per person per day;
$31.80 per person per week
Baths are shared. Linens and maid service are provided.
Pets are not permitted.
Accommodations are available to workshop and
conference groups, and to guests of the University.

MEALS
Cafeteria (typical prices)
Breakfast — $ .85
Lunch — $1.25
Dinner — $1.85

ACTIVITIES (on campus or nearby)
Concerts on campus. Tours of Haeger Potteries. Fishing,
boating, picnicking on Lake Argyle and Spring Lake Parks.

AVAILABLE DATES
June 15 — August 15
Reservations are required.

CONTACT
Student Residence Programs Officer
111 Sherman Hall
Telephone: (309) 298-1826

MONMOUTH COLLEGE
Monmouth, Illinois 61462

Monmouth is located in northwestern Illinois. The city offers many recreational opportunities and leisure-time facilities. There is a fine park which encompasses a challenging 18-hole golf course, baseball diamond, and picnic and playground areas. Approximately 18 miles west lies the Mississippi River, on which the last paddle boat, the Delta Queen, is still afloat. Of great interest to the literary person is the home of Carl Sandburg in Galesburg. An afternoon's trip may take you to nearby New Salem, home of Abraham Lincoln; Nauvoo, the first Mormon Settlement; and the state capital. Nearby are Black Hawk State Park, Sauk Trail, Starved Rock State Park, and other sites of interest.

ACCOMMODATIONS
Single room — $6.00 per person per day
Double room — $5.00 per person per day
Baths are shared. Linens are included. Rooms contain two single beds. Pets, children under 16 years of age, and drinking of alcoholic beverages by persons under 19 years of age are not permitted.
Accommodations are available to students, alumni, adults and prospective matriculants.

MEALS
Cafeteria (typical prices)
Breakfast — $1.00
Lunch — $1.35
Dinner — $1.75

ACTIVITIES (on campus or nearby)
Mississippi River, swimming, tennis, baseball, boating, fishing, bowling and golf.

AVAILABLE DATES
June 1 — July 20

CONTACT
Dean of Students Office
Telephone: (309) 457-2113

NORTH CENTRAL COLLEGE
Naperville, Illinois 60540

Naperville is just 26 miles west of Chicago, making day
and evening trips to this major metropolis an easy matter.
Chicago's first permanent cabin was built about 1779
by Jean Baptiste Point du Sable, a Black explorer and
trader. The terrible Chicago Fire started on October 6,
1871, destroying almost a third of the city. One of the
buildings to survive, the Old Water Tower, may be seen
in midtown. An important collection concerned with the
Civil War and Lincolniana is housed at the Historical
Society building. A section of the famous portage linking
the Great Lakes with the Mississippi River, discovered
by Marquette and Joliet in 1673, is still preserved in the
Forest Preserve District. There are excellent stores on
State Street and on Michigan Avenue, on a par with the
luxurious establishments on New York's Fifth Avenue.
Nightlife is highly varied and exciting, and there are
numerous summer concerts and theatre presentations,
as well as professional sports.

ACCOMMODATIONS
Single room — $8.50 per person per day
Double room — $4.50 per person per day
Baths are shared. Linens are provided: $1.00 per set
of sheets per day.
Accommodations are available to groups and conferences.

MEALS
Cafeteria (typical prices)
All meals included in a $6.00 per person per day fee.

ACTIVITIES (on campus or nearby)
On campus: volley ball and gym. Sightseeing in Chicago.

AVAILABLE DATES

CONTACT
Mr. Dan Cornthwaite
Director of Summer Housing
Telephone: (312) 355-5500, ext. 52

BRADLEY UNIVERSITY
Peoria, Illinois 61606

Peoria is on Interstate 74 and the Illinois Waterway.
This lifeline in the nation's heartland winds some 330
toll-free miles from the Mississippi River up the Illinois
and Des Plaines Rivers joining Lake Michigan at Chicago,
thus linking two of North America's most important
shipping routes—the Mississippi River and St. Lawrence
Seaway. At Peoria a steady procession of barges plying
the waterway with their cargoes of coal, petroleum
products, grain, sand, gravel, chemicals and iron ore
can be seen. The city has an active cultural life, with
numerous performances of ballet, symphony, drama and
art, and a wide variety of recreational opportunities.

ACCOMMODATIONS
Single room—$7.00 per person per day;
$49.00 per person per week
Double room—$5.00 per person per day;
$35.00 per person per week
Baths are shared. Pets are not permitted.
Accommodations are available to students, alumni, adults,
families and prospective matriculants.

MEALS
Cafeteria (typical prices)

Breakfast	—	$1.00 - $1.50
Lunch	—	$1.50 - $2.20
Dinner	—	$1.80 - $2.50

ACTIVITIES (on campus or nearby)
Swimming, fishing, tennis, hiking, family picnics,
weekend trips and scenic tours.

AVAILABLE DATES
May 20—August 20
Advance reservations are required.

CONTACT
Mr. Jack Kuntz
Conference Director, Student Center
Telephone: (309) 676-7611, extension 333 or 327

TRI-STATE COLLEGE
Angola, Indiana 46703

Angola, in the northeastern-most corner of Indiana, is approximately 12 miles from both the Michigan and Ohio state lines. This is rural Mid-West vacationland at its best. It abounds with spring-fed lakes, rolling hills, wheat fields and grazing sheep. An 18-hole championship golf course and tennis courts provide outdoor recreation.

ACCOMMODATIONS
Single room—$5.00 per person per day
Double room—$4.50 per person per day
(double rooms have twin beds)
Baths are shared. Linens are included. There is no charge for children under 12 years of age using the same room as parents.
Accommodations are available to students, alumni, adults, families and prospective matriculants.

MEALS
Cafeteria (typical prices)
Breakfast — $ .90
Lunch — $1.35
Dinner — $1.75

ACTIVITIES (on campus or nearby)
Campus golf course, indoor pool, tennis courts and an athletic area. Surrounding lakes are a short drive, featuring fishing, boating, and the Indiana State Park. Much of the county is a State Game Reserve containing waterfowl migratory flyways.

AVAILABLE DATES
June 15—September 1
All college facilities are available during September except the cafeteria.
Advance reservations are preferred.

CONTACT
Mr. Earl Sharrow
Director, Extended Services
Telephone: (219) 665-3141

INDIANA UNIVERSITY
Bloomington, Indiana 47401

Bloomington, a major center of the electronics and
appliance industries, is surrounded by the limestone
quarries and mills that played a large part in its past.
The 11,000-acre Lake Monroe is situated to the north
of Bloomington, with Yellowwood State Forest and
McCormick's Creek State Park within a 15-mile radius.
Located in the middle of a geographic triangle between
Indianapolis, Louisville and Cincinnati, Bloomington
offers the numerous cultural advantages of a university
town, as well as the outdoor activities of Lake Monroe
dam and reservoir.

ACCOMMODATIONS
Single room — $5.00 per person per day
Double room — $4.50 per person first day,
$3.50 per day thereafter
Pets and alcoholic beverages are not permitted. Linens
and maid service are included.
Accommodations are available to students, alumni, adults,
prospective matriculants and a limited number of families.

MEALS
Cafeteria (typical prices)
Breakfast — $ .90
Lunch — $1.65
Dinner — $1.95
A coffee shop at the Indiana Union is available.

ACTIVITIES (on campus or nearby)
Brown County Playhouse, Brown County State Park;
tennis, golf (small fees are charged for both), swimming
at indoor and outdoor pools.

AVAILABLE DATES
May 15 — August 10
Advance reservations are required.

CONTACT
Mr. Ross Smith
801 North Jordan Avenue
Telephone: (812) 337-2712

UNIVERSITY OF EVANSVILLE
Evansville, Indiana 47714

The University is located in a residential area of the
city of Evansville in southwestern Indiana on the Ohio
River. Evansville is 170 miles from Indianapolis; 110 from
Louisville, Kentucky; 160 from Nashville, Tennessee;
and 180 from St. Louis. Interesting sites include Santa
Claus, Indiana; Lincoln's boyhood home and Lincoln
State Park; New Harmony, Indiana, the site of two early
experiments in communal living; and Wyandotte Cave.

ACCOMMODATIONS
Double room—$4.25 per person per day.
Baths are shared and linens are included. Pets are not
permitted.

MEALS
Cafeteria (typical prices)
Breakfast — $1.25
Lunch — $1.95
Dinner — $2.30

ACTIVITIES (on campus or nearby)
Swimming, tennis, and use of most university gymnastic
facilities. Public golf courses nearby.

AVAILABLE DATES
June 1—August 15
Advance reservations are preferred.

CONTACT
Mr. Robert Reading
Conference Office
1800 Lincoln Avenue
Telephone: (812) 479-2956

NORTHWOOD INSTITUTE OF INDIANA
West Baden Springs, Indiana 47469

The Institute is housed in a spectacular building which
far exceeds the scope of the American Palace Era.
The building has been called the eighth wonder of the
world and is certainly wondrous. It's an enormous
circular structure with six floors and 708 rooms, all of
which face the central court—a vast Pompeiian atrium,
over 208 feet in diameter, with pillars, balconies, a marble
floor and a towering 150-foot high domed roof. This
flamboyant edifice was built by Col. Lee Sinclar in 1902
and functioned as a hotel until the Depression. Shortly
thereafter it was sold—for $1.00—to the Society of Jesus
and ultimately became the Northwood Institute. It is now
undergoing restoration with the aim of making it a
living museum. The Institute is an experience, unique
in modern America, which no one should miss.

ACCOMMODATIONS
Single room—$3.50 per person per day;
$24.50 per person per week
Double room—$2.50 per person per day;
$17.50 per person per week
Showers are shared. Linens are provided for $1.00
additional. Pets and alcoholic beverages are not permitted.
Accommodations are available to the general public.

MEALS
Cafeteria (typical prices)
Breakfast — $1.00
Lunch — $1.25
Dinner — $1.50
The above prices are for when school is in session.
There are also restaurants off campus.

ACTIVITIES (on campus or nearby)
Tennis, golfing at the French Lick Sheraton Hotel, hiking
and boating at Tucker State Park, tours of this fantastic
building.

AVAILABLE DATES
Year round; by appointment September — May.
Advance reservations are required.

CONTACT
Raymond T. Semmens
Director of Outside Activities
Telephone: (812) 036 0071

UNIVERSITY OF DUBUQUE
Dubuque, Iowa 52001

Dubuque's leadership in Iowa was first established as the home of the first bank and newspaper. Later-day developments include dairy farming, meat packing and various industries. The mighty Mississippi River flows past Dubuque, lending her shores and marine beauty to cities and villages on her banks. Dubuque sprawls over high bluffs bordering the river. The hills are so steep that in places sidewalks become staircases, and a quaint cable car is still in operation. Dubuque has recently been named a Bi-Centennial City.

ACCOMMODATIONS
Single room — $3.00 per person per day
Double room — $2.50 per person per day
Baths are shared. Linens are included.
Accommodations are available to students, alumni, adults, families and prospective matriculants.

MEALS
The Student Union is open during the summer. There is a barbecue pit on campus for guest's use.

ACTIVITIES (on campus or nearby)
Boating, fishing, swimming and several city parks.

AVAILABLE DATES
June 1 — August 1

CONTACT
Mr. Larry Hook
Men's Housing Coordinator
Telephone: (319) 557-2342 or (319) 557-2347

NORTHWESTERN COLLEGE
Orange City, Iowa 51041

Orange City is in the rich farming and cattle feeding area of Iowa. It's a Dutch community and has a lovely Tulip Time festival during the third week of May. While here, visit nearby West Bend to see the Grotto of the Redemption which attracts a multitude of visitors each year. Conceived and begun by the Rev. P. R. Dobberstein, the Grotto covers a square city block. It's constructed of ornamental stone from every state and country and relates the story of the "fall and redemption of man." It is believed to be the largest single collection of petrified materials and fossils, shells and minerals in the world. Sioux City is about 40 miles away. While visiting there, don't miss the Floyd Monument, War Eagle's Grave, and Stone State Park where you will get a spectacular view of three states.

ACCOMMODATIONS
Single room — $5.50 per person per day;
$25.00 per person per week
Double room — $4.50 per person per day;
$22.00 per person per week
Pets are not permitted; no smoking in the dormitories. Accommodations are available to students, alumni, adults, families, small children, prospective matriculants.

ACTIVITIES (on campus or nearby)
Tennis courts on campus. Swimming in the town pool. A golf course is 3 miles from campus. Tulip Time: 3rd week in May.

AVAILABLE DATES
May 15 — August 15
Reservations are required.

CONTACT
Paul Muyskens, Business Manager
Business Office
Telephone: (712) 727-4821

SPENCER SCHOOL OF BUSINESS
Spencer, Iowa 51301

The Northwestern lake area where Iowa, Minnesota and
South Dakota join, offers a myriad of activities for
vacationing. Lake Okoboji, one of the three largest blue
water lakes in the world, is 15 miles north of Spencer,
its uppermost section butting into Minnesota. Little Sioux
River, upon whose banks the town of Spencer is situated,
flows from south to north through the fertile midwest
farmlands which produce soybeans, corn and other grains
for trading in the world commodities market. Spencer also
plays host to the world's largest grass-roots county fair,
Clay County.

ACCOMMODATIONS
Apartments — $10 to $20 per person per day;
$50 to $60 per person per week
Pets are not permitted.
Accommodations are available to students, alumni,
adults, families and prospective matriculants.

MEALS
Apartment is equipped with kitchen facilities.

ACTIVITIES (on campus or nearby)
Skiing, fishing, swimming, boating (all free of charge),
Arnolds Park (summer amusements), roof garden
(dancing), and fine arts. Equipment rental is available
at all resort areas.

AVAILABLE DATES
June 1 — September 1
Advance reservations are not required.

CONTACT
Mr. J. R. Grove
217 West Fifth Street
Telephone: (712) 262-7290

KANSAS STATE COLLEGE OF PITTSBURG
Pittsburg, Kansas 66072

On the southeastern corner of Kansas near the Missouri border, Pittsburg, a well known coal center, is also a prosperous educational, farm and industrial community. The Crawford County Museum vividly depicts the coal mining era, providing a comprehensive overview of all phases of the coal and strip mining operations. A state quail farm and two state parks offer attractive game and recreational facilities.

ACCOMMODATIONS
Single room — $4.00 per person per day
Double room — $4.00 per person per day
The cost of each room is the same per person per day regardless of the number of guests. Baths are shared or private. Pets, children under 12 years of age, and alcoholic beverages are not permitted.
Accommodations are available to students, alumni, adults, families and prospective matriculants.

MEALS
Cafeteria (typical prices)
Breakfast — $1.25
Lunch — $1.50
Dinner — $1.75
A coffee shop is available.

ACTIVITIES (on campus or nearby)
Tennis, swimming, golf and fishing.

AVAILABLE DATES
Available year-round, although types of accommodations will vary depending on time of year.
Advance reservations are required.

CONTACT
Housing Office
112 Russ Hall
Telephone: (316) 231-7000

BEREA COLLEGE
Berea, Kentucky 40403

Berea is located in the foothills of the Cumberland
Mountains "where the Bluegrass meets the mountains."
It's a small town, founded in 1855, with the college and
the handweaving industry as the main source of income.
The college is tuition-free; each student works a minimum
of 10 hours a week in the Student Craft Industries —
a bakery, dairy farm, and shops for weaving, wood-
working, needlecraft, broomcraft, ceramics and printing.
Be sure to see the college's Art Department Galleries,
Science Building, Craft Demonstration Center and the
Appalachian Museum. The area contains several cultural
and historic sites: Churchill Weavers, the largest handweaving firm in the country; Great Saltpeter Cave,
a spur of the Big Hill Range; Fort Boonesboro State
Park, a restored pioneer village; Pleasant Hill, a restored
Shaker village; and the Cumberland Falls.

ACCOMMODATIONS
Single room — $6.60 per person per day;
$39.60 per person per week
Double room — $4.40 per person per day;
$26.40 per person per week
Baths are shared. Linens are provided. Pets and
intoxicants are not permitted.
Accommodations are available to non-profit groups
of 10 or more.

MEALS
Cafeteria (typical prices)
Breakfast — $1.00
Lunch — $1.75
Dinner — $2.00
There is also a snack bar and restaurant located
on campus.

ACTIVITIES (on campus or nearby)
14 tennis courts, indoor pool, softball, baseball fields,
cinder track, outdoor pool, 9 hole golf course, hiking trails,
cookout facilities, Paul Green's outdoor drama
"Wilderness Road" nightly, excluding Sundays, at
Indian Fort Theater.

AVAILABLE DATES
Early June — August
Advance reservations are suggested.

CONTACT
R. V. Pettys, Asst. to the Business Vice President
CPO 1538, Telephone: (606) 986-9341

KENTUCKY

SPALDING COLLEGE
Louisville, Kentucky 40203

Louisville, founded in 1778 by Col. George Rogers Clark, is the home of the famous Kentucky Derby, begun in 1875, which takes place the first Saturday in May each year. The Derby is preceded by ten days of gala festivities. Don't miss Farmington, a 14-room home designed by Thomas Jefferson; Locust Grove, Col. Clark's retirement home; Zachary Taylor National Cemetery which contains his tomb; Otter Creek Park; the Zoological Garden; Cherokee Park, considered the most beautiful of Louisville's parks; Iroquois Park which provides a great view of the city; Kentucky Railway Museum which contains vintage locomotives and railroad cars, circa 1870; and the J. B. Speed Art Museum. An old sternwheeler, the *Belle of Louisville*, provides 2½-hour cruises on the Ohio River. The *Belle* and the *Delta Queen* hold an annual race during the Derby Festival.

ACCOMMODATIONS
Single room — $7.00 per person per day;
$49.00 per person per week
Double room — $5.00 per person per day;
$35.00 per person per week
Baths are shared. Linens are provided. Pets and alcoholic beverages are not permitted.
Accommodations are available to students, alumni, families and prospective matriculants.

MEALS
Cafeteria (typical prices)
Breakfast — $1.50
Lunch — $1.75
Dinner — $2.00
There are also many snack bars and restaurants located off campus.

ACTIVITIES (on campus or nearby)
Louisville Theatre, restaurants, sports arena, churches, downtown shopping area.

AVAILABLE DATES
Year round.
Reservations are suggested.

CONTACT
Sr. Ann Legeay, Residence Director
947 South 4th Street
Telephone: (502) 585-9911

LOYOLA UNIVERSITY — NEW ORLEANS
New Orleans, Louisiana 70118

New Orleans — Rampart Street, Dixieland Jazz, the Quarter, the Mardi Gras — is an entrancing city. It's famous for delicious creole cooking and for an elegant evening dine at Brennan's (the building dates from 1795) or at Antoine's. Stroll down Pirate's Alley (Orlean's Alley), a favorite spot for painters. Visit St. Louis Cathedral, one of the most famous cathedrals in the United States. Have a confection and some of the famous New Orleans' chicory coffee at the Morning Call, a well-known gathering place which never closes. Browse in the New Orleans Jazz Museum and listen to traditional New Orleans jazz concerts, given nightly at Preservation Hall. Walk through St. Anthony's Garden and the notorious Dueling Oaks, both famous for the many "affairs of honor" settled there. Walk down Rue Royale where fine antiques, laces and other interesting items may be purchased. The college is in the garden district, near the Quarter and other historic sites

ACCOMMODATIONS
Single room — $3.50 per person per day;
$24.50 per person per week
Double room — $2.75 per person per day;
$19.25 per person per week
Baths are shared. Linens are provided for $1.50 deposit. Maid service is provided in the fee. No pets are permitted. Accommodations are available to the general public.

MEALS
Cafeteria (typical prices)
Breakfast — $1.50
Lunch — $1.85
Dinner — $2.20
This is a SAGA food service: unlimited portions.

ACTIVITIES (on campus or nearby)
Sightseeing and other activities in the city. Nearby are facilities for swimming, parks, golf, tennis — all within walking distance.

AVAILABLE DATES
June 1 — August 1
Reservations are suggested.

CONTACT
Richard Lawton, Housing Director
6363 St. Charles Avenue
Telephone: (504) 866-5471

TULANE UNIVERSITY
New Orleans, Louisiana 70118

New Orleans is one of the largest ports in the United
States, the main distribution point in the South, and a
marketing center for many of the nation's products.
It is beautifully situated along Pontchartrain Lake and
the Mississippi River, and is renowned for its Basin,
Canal and Rampart Streets jazz. New Orleans' old
mansions are notable for their lovely iron grillwork,
particularly those in the Vieux Carre (Latin Quarter).
Beauregard Square, next to the Latin Quarter, was the
Sunday gathering place for the slaves in the ante bellum
period. The colorful French Market is the place to wind
up a day or night, drinking the famous New Orleans
coffee at one of the old coffee spots. Jackson Square,
in the center of the Quarter, where the large statue of
Andrew Jackson was placed in 1856, is the artists' quarter.
Here visitors can view displays of local artists hung on
the decorative iron grillwork fences. Don't miss the
New Orleans Jazz Museum on Conte Street, where you
can listen to rare jazz pieces and commentary, and
enjoy the house's architectural delights.

ACCOMMODATIONS
Single room — $6.25 per person per day
Double room — $4.75 per person per day
Baths are shared. Linens and maid service are provided.
Pets are not permitted.
Accommodations are available to students (who can
show a valid I.D. card) and large groups (up to 1,000)
with educational interests. No children under 12 years
of age.

MEALS
Prices are not available — all meals are a la carte.
Many eating facilities are located off campus.

ACTIVITIES (on campus or nearby)
Sightseeing.

AVAILABLE DATES
July 1 — July 30
Reservations are suggested.

CONTACT
Summer Conference Manager
Telephone: (504) 865-4591

BOWDOIN COLLEGE
Brunswick, Maine 04011

Brunswick, just northeast of the Casco Bay resort area, is a community where commerce, industry and education flourish in well-balanced proportions. Summer events on campus include the Brunswick Music Theatre and chamber music concerts. In town are many imposing Federalist mansions, while tree-lined Maine Street, with many interesting shops, is one of the widest in New England. Portland, largest city in Maine and one of the most interesting and historic towns in New England, is 26 miles to the south.

ACCOMMODATIONS
Three bedroom apartment — $125.00 per week
Baths are private. Linens are included. Maid service is available. Pets are not permitted.
Accommodations are available to students, alumni, adults, families and prospective matriculants.

MEALS
Kitchenettes are included with accommodations.

ACTIVITIES (on campus or nearby)
Indoor pool, tennis courts, summer theatre (musicals) on campus in July and August. Museum of Art, Peary-McMillan Arctic Museum (open daily), Harriet Beecher Stowe House, Hawthorne House, First Parish Church; Atlantic Ocean is 10 minutes away.

AVAILABLE DATES
July 1 — August 25
Advance reservations are required.

CONTACT
Mrs. Mary C. Bernier
Hawthorne-Longfellow Hall
Telephone: (207) 725-8731, extension 264

UNIVERSITY OF MAINE AT FORT KENT
Fort Kent, Maine 04743

Fort Kent is the principal town of Maine's "Far North," at the northern terminus of US Route 1 and the confluence of the St. John River. It's the gateway to the famed Allagash Wilderness and is a commercial center for fishing, hunting, farming and lumbering. There are antique hand tools and displays at Fort Kent Block House, a fort built in 1839 during the Aroostook contretemps with England. You can take long or short trips up the St. John and Allagash Rivers for trout and you can hunt, hike, fish for salmon and explore the lake chain along Fish River. Bear, deer, grouse and other wildlife can be hunted in the hinterland. Fort Kent is the southern end of the St. John-Allagash canoe trip which starts 156 miles away at East Seboomook on Moosehead Lake. The area is superb for outdoors people.

ACCOMMODATIONS
Single room — $18.50 per person per week
Double room — $17.50 per person per week
Baths are shared.
Accommodations are available to the general public.

MEALS
Cafeteria (typical prices)
Breakfast — $1.00
Lunch — $1.25
Dinner — $1.75

ACTIVITIES (on campus or nearby)
Tennis, golf, canoeing, fishing. Canoes may be rented. Tours, guides and equipment for activities listed in description may be arranged.

AVAILABLE DATES
Write to school for information.
Reservations are required.

CONTACT
Raymond Dumais
Pleasant Street
Telephone: (207) 834-3162

UNITY COLLEGE
Unity, Maine 04988

Unity is located in the heart of Maine on U.S. Route 202.
It is 20 miles from Augusta, 20 miles from Bangor,
40 miles from Camden, one of Maine's lovelier seacoast
towns and a two hour drive from Acadia National Park
and Bar Harbor. For a day between excursions, the
vacationer can remain in Unity and enjoy excellent
fishing, swimming and boating on Lake Winnecook.

ACCOMMODATIONS
Single room — $4.50 per person per day;
$27.00 per person per week (6 day week)
Double room — $3.50 per person per day;
$21.00 per person per week (6 day week)
Baths are shared. Linens are $2.50 additional.
Accommodations are available to students, alumni, adults,
families and prospective matriculants.

ACTIVITIES (on campus or nearby)
Swimming, fishing, tennis and hiking. Scenic tours may be
arranged. Canoes are available for rent. Other activities
include Monmouth Theatre, Pittsfield Egg Festival,
Belfast Lobster Festival and Bangor Arts Festival.

AVAILABLE DATES
July 1 — August 20
Advance reservations are required.

CONTACT
Mr. Alan M. Vannini
Administration Building
Quaker Hill Road
Telephone: (207) 948-3131, extension 25

LOYOLA COLLEGE
Baltimore, Maryland 21210

The strategic location between north and south made Baltimore important during the Civil War. The nation's first railroad, The Baltimore and Ohio, was incorporated in this city in 1827. Baltimore was a political center, and seven presidents were nominated here. It has become a leading east coast shipping city, with industry and manufacturing employing a significant part of the labor force.

ACCOMMODATIONS
Single occupancy — $9.00 per person per day
Double occupancy — $6.00 per person per day
Baths are shared. Pets are not permitted.
Accommodations are available to students, alumni, adults, families and prospective matriculants.

MEALS
Cafeteria (typical prices)
Breakfast — $1.75
Lunch — $2.25
Dinner — $3.25

ACTIVITIES (on campus or nearby)
Swimming (a fee of $15.00 is charged for group use of swimming pool and service of lifeguard), tennis, and use of athletic fields. Fort McHenry (home of the "Star Spangled Banner"), Baltimore harbor (third largest in the east), Annapolis and the U.S. Naval Academy are 25 miles away, and Washington, D.C. is 40 miles away. There are a number of dinner theaters nearby.

AVAILABLE DATES
June 1 — August 15

CONTACT
Mrs. Margery W. Harriss
Coordinator of Special Events
4501 North Charles Street
Telephone: (301) 323-1010

MORGAN STATE COLLEGE
Baltimore, Maryland 21239

Baltimore was the scene of two "firsts" in American history: the first railroad station and the first telegraph message ("What Hath God Wrought"). It also contains the oldest Catholic cathedral in the nation, the Basilica of the Assumption, and the third oldest synagogue, Lloyd Street Synagogue. Fort McHenry, a national monument, was completed in 1803 and was used from the War of 1812 through World War II. Its successful resistance to a British seige in the War of 1812 became the inspiration for our national anthem by Francis Scott Key. The Bullets, Clippers, Colts and Orioles provide plenty of sports excitement during their seasons, and there are many cultural activities in the city, notably the Symphony Orchestra, drama presentations, and ballet.

ACCOMMODATIONS
Single room—only a few available, rates not provided
Double room—$5.00 per person per day
Baths are shared; some of the rooms have sinks.
Linens are provided. Pets and alcoholic beverages are not permitted.
Accommodations are available to groups for conferences, conventions, etc.

MEALS
Cafeteria (typical prices)
Breakfast — $1.00
Lunch — $1.35
Dinner — $1.45
Prices vary. There is also a snack bar and the new Student Center will house a restaurant. Many eating facilities are available off campus.

ACTIVITIES (on campus or nearby)
Swimming, basketball, track, etc.

AVAILABLE DATES
Summer months. Exact dates not available.
Advance reservations are required.

CONTACT
Mr. E. R. Golden
Director of Business Operations
Cold Spring Lane & Hillen Road
Morgan State College
Telephone: (301) 323-2270

WASHINGTON COLLEGE
Chestertown, Maryland 21620

Chestertown is a gracious old village facing the broad
and tranquil Chester River. It's the very essence of the
Eastern Shore with a mellow combination of sights,
feelings, tastes and smells that recall centuries of pleasant
living. Social life and sports are important traditions
here. Nearly everyone has a boat of some kind for fishing,
sailing or shooting. Practically every species of wild duck
which migrates east of the Mississippi River is to be
found in this region. Washington College was founded
in 1782 and received an endowment from General George
Washington. It was in this town on November 9, 1780,
that the Protestant Episcopal Church of America,
as distinguished from the Church of England, was
denominated.

ACCOMMODATIONS
Single room — $6.00 per person per day
Double room — $4.50 per person per day
Baths are shared. Pets are not permitted. Three nights
is the minimum stay.

MEALS
Restaurants and coffee shops are available in the area.

ACTIVITIES (on campus or nearby)
Sailing, fishing, swimming, tennis, indoor sports and
gunning.

AVAILABLE DATES
June 1 — August 15
Advance reservations are required.

CONTACT
Mr. Gene Hessey
Business Manager
Telephone: (301) 778-2800

GARDEN HALLS DORMITORIES
Boston, Massachusetts 02116

Not only is Boston a historic mecca, but it is also one of the most exciting cities in the country. Many colleges and universities line its main streets, and across the Charles River, Cambridge's as well. Historic sites are seemingly without end, and best enjoyed by walking tours, beginning in the famed Boston Commons, Public Gardens and Beacon Hill. Practically every one of the 83 cities and towns in the Boston metropolitan area is tied in with America's past ... Lexington, Concord, Gloucester, Salem. The Boston Public Library and numerous museums are exceptional cultural attractions. And, of course, within short drives are New England coastal attractions, Cape Cod to the south, Marblehead and Rockport among many exciting north shore locales.

ACCOMMODATIONS
Single room — $5.00 per person per day;
$35.00 per person per week
Double room — $3.50 per person per day;
$17.50 per person per week
Minimum $25.00
Baths are both shared and private. Linen included.
Accommodations are available to students, alumni, adults, families and prospective matriculants.

MEALS
Restaurants and coffee shop are in the area.

ACTIVITIES (on campus or nearby)
Golf, swimming, boating and baseball.

AVAILABLE DATES
June 15 — August 15
Advance reservations are required.

CONTACT
Mrs. Edith Moody
Garden Halls Dormitories
163 Marlborough Street
Telephone: (617) 266-5232, or (617) 267-0079

NORTHEASTERN UNIVERSITY
Boston, Massachusetts 02115

Boston has an excellent walking tour that leads the visitor to most of the sites connected with this city's history as the birthplace of the American Revolution. Here the so-called "Boston Massacre" took place in 1770, fanning the passions of the 13 Colonies. The Boston Tea Party, in 1773, set the stage for the coming war. On April 18-19, 1775, Paul Revere, Samuel Prescott and William Dawes brought the news to Lexington and Concord that English General Thomas Gage was preparing to march his army upon Concord. The war had begun. The Battles of Lexington and Concord were closely followed by the Battle of Bunker Hill, and the British forces, under General William Howe, evacuated Boston on March 17, 1776.

ACCOMMODATIONS
Single room — $6.00 per person per day
Double room — $5.00 per person per day
Baths are shared. Sheets are provided; no blankets or pillows.
Accommodations are available to conference groups with an educational affiliation.

MEALS
Information is not available.

ACTIVITIES (on campus or nearby)
Sightseeing in Boston and famous historical sites nearby.

AVAILABLE DATES
Mid-June — July 31
Reservations are required.

CONTACT
J. Veryzer
Coordinator of Housing
360 Huntington Avenue
Telephone: (617) 437-2597

SIMMONS COLLEGE
Boston, Massachusetts 02115

Historians, scholars and music lovers all ... Boston hails you. Its history is deeply embedded in U.S. archives. The Boston Tea Party and American Revolution strongly typify Boston's significant role in the growth of our country. Several Declaration of Independence signers were Bostonians. Harvard and M.I.T., among the world's leading educational institutions, are located across the Charles River in Cambridge. Many streets in Boston are literally lined with other colleges and universities. The Boston Symphony is in residence at Symphony Hall in the fall, winter and spring seasons, then moves to their summer home, Tanglewood, in the Berkshire Mountains for a season of concerts under its world famous, open-air shed. The nearness of Cape Cod and Massachusetts Bay provide pleasure and a summer place for vacationers.

ACCOMMODATIONS
Single room—$6.00 per person per day;
$30.00 per person per week
Double room—$5.00 per person per day;
$25.00 per person per week
Baths are shared. Pets are not permitted.
Accommodations are available to students, alumni, adults, families and prospective matriculants.

MEALS
Cafeteria (typical prices)
Breakfast — $ .99
Lunch — $2.00
Dinner — $2.50

ACTIVITIES (on campus or nearby)
Tennis, water sports, skiing, fishing, swimming and horseback riding.

AVAILABLE DATES
May 26—August 27

CONTACT
Mr. E. W. Steer
Business Manager
300 The Fenway
Telephone: (617) 738-2118

WILLISTON-NORTHAMPTON SCHOOL
Easthampton, Massachusetts 01027

Easthampton, just off Interstate 91 and the serene and
verdant Connecticut River Valley, is a typical Massachusetts town with its gleaming white church spires which
bespeak pride in the land and solid workmanship.
Massachusetts has educational resources unexcelled by
any other state. In this area alone are located no less than
six universities and colleges and many of the nation's
foremost independent schools. To the west of Easthampton
is Tanglewood, patriarch of American music festivals
and summer home of the Boston Symphony Orchestra.

ACCOMMODATIONS
Single room — $5.00 per person per day;
$35.00 per person per week
Double room — $5.00 per person per day;
$35.00 per person per week
Dormitory has 20-person capacity. Single beds are
available. Baths are shared. Smoking is not permitted.
Accommodations are available to students, alumni, adults,
families and prospective matriculants.

MEALS
Not provided

ACTIVITIES (on campus or nearby)
Antiquing, tennis, golf, mountain climbing, swimming
and summer theatre.

AVAILABLE DATES
June 5 — August 31
Advance reservations are required.

CONTACT
Business Manager's Office
Telephone: (413) 527-1520, extension 60

STONEHILL COLLEGE
Easton, Massachusetts 02356

Easton, the home of Stonehill College, is in southeastern
Massachusetts, 20 miles south of Boston and minutes by
expressway from Cape Cod. The Cape and Massachusetts
Bay provide a myriad of summer beach and water
activities. Rich in New England history, the town is near
Plymouth. It is a convenient location for exploring
the cultural and recreational attractions of New England,
or horse-racing at the track in nearby Foxboro.

ACCOMMODATIONS
Single room — $7.00 per person per day;
$42.00 per person per week
Double room — $5.00 per person per day;
$30.00 per person per week
Rooms are in small "townehouse" units consisting of a
living room, six bedrooms and two bath rooms. Families
are ordinarily housed in such a way as to provide
bathroom facilities. All rooms have single beds.
A brochure is available on request.
Accommodations are available to students, alumni, adults,
families and prospective matriculants.

MEALS
Cafeteria (typical prices)
Breakfast — $1.00
Lunch — $1.50
Dinner — $2.50

ACTIVITIES (on campus or nearby)
Tennis, swimming, boating, softball, volleyball, squash,
basketball, and summer theatre on campus. Boston, Cape
Cod, Plymouth Plantation and many other historical,
cultural, and recreational opportunities are within
easy day-trip distance.

AVAILABLE DATES
June 15 — August 23
Advance reservations required. No reservations by phone.

CONTACT
Director, Conferences and Institutes Division
Box R
Telephone: (617) 238-2052

BAY PATH JUNIOR COLLEGE
Longmeadow, Massachusetts 01106

The college is just a six-minute drive from the center of Springfield, a major cultural and commercial center of the area. Storrowton, in Springfield, is a reconstructed collection of early New England houses, meetinghouse, country store. Other Springfield sights include: Springfield Armory Museum, a U.S. arsenal containing a collection of small arms from 1795 to modern; George Walter Vincent Smith Art Museum, housing Oriental and European decorative arts; The Museum of Fine Arts and the Science Museum which includes a planetarium, aquarium and a Junior Museum. Fifty miles away from Longmeadow is Worcester, another major business and cultural center. In both Springfield and Worcester, you can golf, swim, picnic, and boat. There's a collection of pewter, toys, gowns, glass and other memorabilia of early Massachusetts in Worcester's Historical Society Museum and an interesting collection of arms, Renaissance armor, and metal crafts dating from the Stone Age to the present in the John Woodman Higgins Armory.

ACCOMMODATIONS
Rates are negotiable — dependent upon size of group and services required.
Accommodations are available to responsible groups of 100-300. Pets are not permitted. Baths are shared. Linens and maid service are included in the fee.

MEALS
Cafeteria (typical prices)
Breakfast — $1.00 to $1.50
Lunch — $1.50 to $3.00
Dinner — $3.50 to $6.00
Prices range according to menu. Facilities include a cafeteria, snack bar and dining hall.

ACTIVITIES (on campus or nearby)
Tanglewood in the Berkshires (Lenox); swimming, boating, fishing, hiking, etc. in the Brimfield and Granville State Forests about one-half hour away.

AVAILABLE DATES
June — August
Reservations must be made well in advance.

CONTACT
Mrs. I. G. Parsons, Conference Coordinator
Telephone: (413) 567-0621

TUFTS UNIVERSITY
Medford, Massachusetts 02155

Near storied Winchester and Lexington, Medford is
six miles northwest of historic downtown Boston on
Interstate 93 and is readily accessible to the educational,
cultural, social and recreational life of that city.
Historical sites are around every corner in the Boston
area, but these are by no means the only attractions
to visitors. Some of the most popular vacation areas in
the East are but a few miles away — Cape Cod, Cape Ann,
New Bedford, Nantucket, Provincetown, Rockport,
Gloucester, among many others.

ACCOMMODATIONS
Single room — $8.00 per person per day;
$56.00 per person per week
Double room — $5.00 per person per day;
$35.00 per person per week
Baths are shared. Pets are not permitted.
Accommodations are available to students, alumni, adults,
families and prospective matriculants.

MEALS (typical prices)
Breakfast — $1.25
Lunch — $1.75
Dinner — $2.50

ACTIVITIES (on campus or nearby)
Tufts Summer Theatre, Boston Symphony Esplanade
Concerts, historical tours, sailing regatta, National
Longwood Tennis Championships, country fairs and nine
museums are some of the area's attractions. In addition
to swimming, fishing, tennis, hiking, sailing and
gymnastics, family picnics, weekend trips, guided scenic
tours, barbecues, and clam bakes are other activities.

AVAILABLE DATES
June 20 — August 20
Advance reservations are required.

CONTACT
Mrs. Marjorie Farley McNiff
Director, Conference Bureau
Telephone: (617) 628-2247 or (617) 628-5000,
extension 146

CURRY COLLEGE
Milton, Massachusetts 02186

Milton, with a population of 27,000, is just south of
Boston and easily accessible to that historic city.
The Adams Historic Site is nearby.

ACCOMMODATIONS
Single room — $4.00 per person per day;
$20.00 per person per week
Double room — $6.00 per person per day;
$30.00 per person per week
Linens are $1.50 additional.
Accommodations are available to students, alumni, adults,
families and prospective matriculants (children 12 years
of age and under are free).

MEALS
Cafeteria (typical prices)
Breakfast — $1.10
Lunch — $1.35
Dinner — $1.75

ACTIVITIES (on campus or nearby)
Swimming, golf, tennis, riding, hiking, fishing and
numerous state and local parks. Greens fee is $3.00; horse-
back riding is $5.00 per hour. Some of the area's scenic,
recreational, historic and cultural attractions are Boston's
Freedom Trail, Bunker Hill Monument, Cape Cod National
Seashore, *U.S.S. Constitution*, Old Sturbridge Village,
Boston Pops and the Boston Symphony Orchestras.

AVAILABLE DATES
June 15 — August 18
Advance reservations are required.

CONTACT
Mr. Robert Capalbo
848 Brush Hill Road
Telephone: (617) 333-0500, extension 252 or 254
(or Mrs. Mary Granskie, extension 238)

ANNA MARIA COLLEGE
Paxton, Massachusetts 01612

The college, on a 290-acre campus in Paxton, is 10 miles from Worcester and within a two-hour's drive of Boston and all the Massachusetts historical sites related to the beginning of the War of Independence. Worcester's Science Center contains an omnisphere with a planetarium, a museum, zoo, botanical gardens and the Hall of Energy. Green Hill Park has a municipal golf course and a barnyard zoo. About 40 miles from Paxton are Concord and Lexington, the birthplace of the nation. In Concord, visit the battleground in the Minute Man National Historical Park, the Great Meadows National Wildlife Refuge, and the Orchard House and School of Philosophy where Louisa May Alcott wrote *Little Women*. Lexington was the scene of the first battle of the Revolution. Look for the Battle Green with its Old Monument and the Boulder marking the Minutemen's line of battle, and the Buckman and Monroe Taverns where the opposing forces mustered before the battle.

ACCOMMODATIONS
Single room — $5.00 per person per day;
$32.00 per person per week
Double room — $4.00 per person per day;
$25.00 per person per week
Extra cot in a room — $3.00 per night.
Pets are not permitted; smoking is restricted.
Baths are shared. Linens are provided in the fee.
Accommodations are available to organized groups.

MEALS
Cafeteria (typical prices)
Breakfast — $1.25
Lunch — $1.75
Dinner — $2.75
Cafeteria is on campus. A restaurant is nearby, off-campus.

ACTIVITIES (on campus or nearby)
The 290-acre campus is ideal for hiking, nature walks, etc. Tennis courts are available, but racquets must be provided by the visitor.

AVAILABLE DATES
June 20 — August 10
Reservations are required.

CONTACT
Mrs. Snell, Director of Housing, Telephone: (617) 757-4586

MERCY COLLEGE OF DETROIT
Detroit, Michigan 48219

Founded in 1700 by the French, Detroit has sprung from
a frontier trading post to one of the nation's major
producers of automobiles, trucks, and tractors. The city
is a five-minute drive through an auto tunnel from
Windsor in Ontario, Canada. A myriad of cultural, sports,
and arts activities greet the visitor wishing to enjoy a
bustling metropolitan holiday. Don't miss: Detroit
Institute of Arts, one of the great art museums,
representing every art-producing country in specific
galleries; the International Institute, with folk dancing
performances; Belle Isle, an enchanting island park
with facilities for almost everything. Stop at the
outstanding Masonic Temple—the largest in the world.
There are concerts all summer long at the Remick
Music Hall on Belle Isle. For an elegant dining
experience, visit the London Chop House.

ACCOMMODATIONS
Single room—$6.24 per person per day
Double room—$5.20 per person per day
Linens are provided. Pets are not permitted.

MEALS
Cafeteria (typical prices)
Breakfast — $1.00
Lunch — $1.50
Dinner — $2.00
Campus food facilities available only during academic
year. There are many restaurants near campus.

ACTIVITIES (on campus or nearby)
Tennis courts available on campus. Off campus: golf,
Detroit Zoological park, amusement parks, State Fair-
grounds. Concerts in Pine Knob and Meadowbrook, movie
theatres, Henry Ford Museum, Stroh's Brewery.

AVAILABLE DATES
Year round.
Advance reservations required.

CONTACT
Ms. Martha Weise
Director of Housing
8200 W. Outer Drive
Box 143

NORTHERN MICHIGAN UNIVERSITY
Marquette, Michigan 49855

Flanked by blueberry plains, forests, and iron and
granite mountains, Marquette rises from the rocky
outcroppings and sandy beaches on the shore of Lake
Superior. Iron ore shipping dominates the dock area.
Named for the 17th century missionary-explorer, the
city has many attractions. Presque Isle Park is on the
lake. The local Historical Society Museum features
pioneer displays and an interesting collection of Upper
Peninsula memorabilia. The John Burt House is open
in the summer. The Sunken Gardens fronting the State
Prison are a replica of a famous garden in Italy.

ACCOMMODATIONS
Single room — $8.00 per person per day;
$40.00 per person per week
Double room — $6.50 per person per day;
$32.50 per person per week
Suite — $2.50 per additional person per day;
$12.50 per additional person per week
Baths are private. Linens and maid service are included.
Pets are not permitted.
Accommodations are available to students, alumni and
prospective matriculants.

MEALS
Cafeteria (typical prices)
Breakfast — $1.25
Lunch — $1.75
Dinner — $2.25
A coffee shop is available.

ACTIVITIES (on campus or nearby)
Tahquamenon Falls, Porcupine Mountains, Pictured
Rocks National Lake Shore, and the Copper Country.
Tennis, hiking, fishing, swimming, archery, bicycling,
boating, camping and bowling. Activity programs include
concerts, plays, exhibits and lectures.

AVAILABLE DATES
June 15 — August 19
Advance reservations are required.

CONTACT
Housing Office
University Center
Telephone: (906) 227-2620

NORTHWOOD INSTITUTE
Midland, Michigan 48640

Midland is situated in the middle of Michigan, 18 miles
from Saginaw Bay and Lake Huron, at the confluence of
four rivers. Many homes and churches in Midland are
architecturally noteworthy. Beneath the area is a brine
sea, important to the local chemical industry. The Midland
Center for the Arts features a dynamic exhibit of
man's history.

ACCOMMODATIONS
Single room — $4.50 to $6.00 per person per day
Double room — $3.00 to $4.50 per person per day
Apartment — $75.00 per week
Baths are private and shared. Linens and maid service
are included in the rental fees.
Accommodations are available to students, alumni, adults,
families and prospective matriculants.

MEALS
Cafeteria (typical prices)
Breakfast — $1.15
Lunch — $1.45
Dinner — $2.00
A coffee shop and catered meals are available.

ACTIVITIES (on campus or nearby)
Emerson Park is located next to the Northwood campus.
Indoor and outdoor tennis, swimming, golf, hiking
and fishing.

AVAILABLE DATES
June 1 — September 1 for groups. Advance reservations
are required.

CONTACT
Mr. Jack Arduin
Special Activities Coordinator
3225 Cook Road
Telephone: (517) 631-1600, extension 279

BEMIDJI STATE COLLEGE
Bemidji, Minnesota 56601

Bemidji is nestled at the foot of the lovely Lake Bemidji
in the midst of Minnesota forest and lake region.
Breathtakingly beautiful country surrounds the city
with excellent camping and hiking, and outstanding
walleye fishing in 1,000 nearby lakes. Take a car tour to
the Red Lake Indian Reservation through "Indian
country." Spend a day enjoying swimming, golf, picnicking,
hiking, fishing, or boating at the Diamond Point Park,
the Cameron Park, or Lake Bemidji State Park.

ACCOMMODATIONS
Single room — $5.50 per person per day;
$29.50 per person per week
Double room — $4.00 per person per day;
$22.00 per person per week
Baths are shared. Linens are provided at no cost (guests
must provide own towels). No pets are permitted.
Accommodations available to the general public.

MEALS
Cafeteria (typical prices)
Breakfast — $1.00
Lunch — $1.50
Dinner — $2.00
Cafeteria and snack bar available on campus,
restaurant off campus.

ACTIVITIES (on campus or nearby)
Swimming from 4 local beaches (two on campus) — free.
Boating (50¢ per hour), tennis courts, fishing.
Most equipment can be rented locally, especially boats,
canoes, etc.

AVAILABLE DATES
June — August 24
Advance reservations are required.

CONTACT
Dr. Larry L. Mangus, Director of Housing
Walnut Hall
Telephone: (218) 755-2030

COLLEGE OF SAINT SCHOLASTICA
Duluth, Minnesota 55811

Fringed by Minnesota's great North Woods, Duluth is a busy world port—the gateway between the Northwest and the Atlantic Ocean for navigation via Lake Superior and the Saint Lawrence Seaway. Now one of the largest harbors in the world in point of tonnage, Duluth is at the axis of the taconite industry, the conversion of low grade iron ore into commercially usable pellets. With its built-in summer comfort factor, the nearby wilderness and hundreds of lakes, Duluth offers unlimited recreational possibilities. The finest canoe country in the United States, the Boundary Waters canoe area, is to the north on U.S. Route 61. Some of the area's scenic, recreational, historic and cultural attractions include Skyline Drive, St. Louis County Historical Society, Railroad Museum, area Cultural Center, Tweed Gallery at the University of Minnesota, Historical Trading Post, Chisholm Museum, and boating on Lake Superior .

ACCOMMODATIONS
Single room — $9.00 per person per day;
$45.00 per person per week
Double room — $5.00 per person per day;
$25.00 per person per week
Apartment — $75.00 for 4 persons per week
(not available daily)
Baths are shared. Pets are not permitted.
Accommodations are available to students, alumni, adults, families and prospective matriculants.

MEALS
Cafeteria (typical prices)
Breakfast — $1.25
Lunch — $1.75
Dinner — $2.25

ACTIVITIES (on campus or nearby)
Swimming, fishing, tennis courts and hiking trails.
Family picnics, weekend trips and guided scenic tours available only through community resources.

AVAILABLE DATES
June 20 — September 15
Advance reservations are required.

CONTACT
Director of Housing
Somers Hall
1200 Kenwood Avenue
Telephone: (218) 728-3631, extension 391

MANKATO STATE COLLEGE
Mankato, Minnesota 56001

Summer home of the Minnesota Vikings, Mankato is situated in the Minnesota River Valley. It is an industrial and farming market center. Mankato pleasantly blends professionalism, industrial and farming activities into a well-rounded northern United States community. The Twin Cities of Minneapolis and St. Paul are approximately 70 miles to the north, lending their new cultural center and urban sophistication to visitors.

ACCOMMODATIONS
Single room — $5.00 per person per day
Double room — $4.00 per person per day
Baths are shared. Linens are included. Pets are not permitted.
Accommodations are available to students, alumni, adults, families and prospective matriculants.

MEALS
Cafeteria (typical prices)
Breakfast — $ .85
Lunch — $1.00
Dinner — $1.50
These meals are available in the cafeteria during the school year.
A coffee shop is available.

ACTIVITIES (on campus or nearby)
Pool, tennis courts, lakes, bowling, sliding, curling, four golf courses and state parks.

AVAILABLE DATES
Facilities are available year-round.
Advance reservations are preferred.

CONTACT
Miss Diane Veronda
Office of Residential Life
Telephone: (507) 389-1011

COLLEGE OF ST. THERESA
Winona, Minnesota 55987

Winona is located in the southeast corner of Minnesota on the banks of the Mississippi River. It's situated on one of the most scenic stretches of the Mississippi River Valley. Climb to Garvin Heights Lookout for a splendid view of the area. While in Winona visit the Historical Society Museum which has Indian artifacts, logging and lumbering exhibits, a country store, music shops, and a blacksmith; the Julius C. Wilkie Steamboat, a steamboat transformed into a museum, which houses Robert Fulton memorabilia and steam engine and boat models; the Bunnell House containing mid-19th century furnishings; the rural schoolhouse, pioneer homestead, farm tool exhibit, antique machinery, and covered bridge all housed at the Arches Branch Museum. There are plenty of outdoor activities available nearby: float and boat fishing, swimming, picnicking and hiking at Lake Winona and Whitman Dam and Locks.

ACCOMMODATIONS
Single and double rooms are available. Check the college for fees.
Smoking is restricted to certain areas. Baths are shared.
Accommodations are available to the general public.

MEALS
Breakfast, lunch and dinner are available at a cafeteria on campus. Prices vary.

ACTIVITIES (on campus or nearby)
Swimming, fishing, hiking, boating, golf and tennis.
Community theatre and concerts in Winona.

AVAILABLE DATES
Summer months.
Reservations are required, one month in advance.

CONTACT
Sister Johnita Klingler
Vice President for Student Affairs
Telephone: (507) 454-2930

SAINT MARY'S COLLEGE
Winona, Minnesota 55987

Winona, still retaining the flavor of its New England
and German settlers, is today an important industrial
and business center just north of Interstate 90 on the
Mississippi River. Picturesquely located on a broad,
level terrace at the foot of steep bluffs rising 500 to 600
feet above the river, Winona offers the many attractions
of the upper Mississippi. Nearby are a wildlife and fish
refuge, Lake Winona, and a 284 mile swatch of hills and
bluffs that hem the river with wilderness. Local exhibits
feature pioneer, Indian, steamboat and lumbering history.

ACCOMMODATIONS
Single room—$4.00 per person per day;
$17.00 per person per week
Double room—$3.50 per person per day;
$15.00 per person per week
Two-bedroom apartment with kitchenette—
$15.00 per night; $60.00 per week
Baths are shared with room accommodations and are
private in apartments only. Linens are approximately
$1.75. Pets are not permitted.
Accommodations are available to families, students,
alumni, adults, and prospective matriculants.

MEALS
Cafeteria (typical prices)
available only during the six week summer session
Breakfast — $1.35
Lunch — $1.65
Dinner — $2.85

ACTIVITIES (on campus or nearby)
Swimming, fishing, tennis and hiking. Children under
18 are required to purchase a button for the swimming
pool (fee $1.00 refundable when button is returned).
Family picnics may be arranged through food service.
Rental available for tents, sleeping bags, canoes, etc.
Some special events on campus or nearby are carnivals,
parades and boat races of "Steamboat Days" in Winona,
usually second weekend in July.

AVAILABLE DATES
June 1—August 15
Advance reservations are required.

CONTACT
Mr. R. J. Nankivil, Vice President for Financial Affairs
Saint Mary's Hall
Telephone: (507) 452-4430, extension 222

WINONA STATE COLLEGE
Winona, Minnesota 55987

Winona rests on the west bank of the Mississippi River,
bordered north and south by the imposing hills of the
beautiful Hiawatha Valley. Towering above Winona are
the limestone bluffs carved out eons ago by the Mississippi
River. This is a paradoxical and beautiful place to visit:
rolling river, placid lake, soaring bluffs and peaceful
valley. Don't miss the annual Steamboat Days here, the
second week of July, when the bygone era is evoked with
shows, parades, boat races, and carnival. Rochester is
about an hour's drive from Winona. It's internationally
famous for its medical facility at the Mayo Institutions.
While there, visit Mayowood, the 38-room former home of
the Mayo brothers; the Hemp Antique Vehicle Museum;
the Historical Center and Museum which features
Norwegian folk arts and a mid-19th century log cabin.
There are nearby county parks for outdoor sports
and picnicking.

ACCOMMODATIONS
Single room — $7.00 per person per day
Double room — $5.00 per person per day
A special student rate is available upon presentation of
college identification.
Pets are not permitted. Baths are shared. Linens are
included.
Accommodations are available to the general public.

MEALS
Cafeteria (typical prices)
Breakfast — $1.25
Lunch — $1.50
Dinner — $2.00
A cafeteria, snack bar and restaurant are on campus.
Other restaurants are in Winona.

ACTIVITIES (on campus or nearby)
On campus: swimming, tennis, gym facilities. Boating,
swimming, fishing, hiking are available at nearby parks:
small fees. Westfield golf course: small fee. Equipment
may be rented.

AVAILABLE DATES
Summer months. The college indicates that there is a
possibility that facilities may be available year round.
Reservations are suggested.

OONTAOT
Ms. J. A. Woodsend, Housing Director
106 Samsen Street
Telephone: (507) 457-2039

CENTRAL METHODIST COLLEGE
Fayette, Missouri 65248

Fayette is a very small town located in the heart of
Missouri. It is near the Missouri River and sits in the
great open plains of the state. Cattle and hogs are the
main source of income of the area. Columbia, about 40
miles away, is a university and college town. Of special
interest on the University of Missouri campus are the
Rare Book Room in Ellis Library, the Museum of Art
and Archaeology, the Museum of Anthropology, the
Journalism Historical Museum, and University Research
Park. Stephens College campus houses the Davis Art
Gallery and the Playhouse, which presents plays starring
students and local professionals. Columbia has an 18 hole
golf course and industrial tours, offered by the
Chamber of Commerce.

ACCOMMODATIONS
Single room — $7.50 per person per day;
for full room and board — $12.00 daily; $70.00 weekly
Double room — $12.00 per person per day,
includes full room and board.
Baths are shared Linens are provided.
Accommodations are available to groups and conferences.

MEALS
Cafeteria (typical prices)
Meals are included in above rates for full room and
board. There are restaurants located off campus.

ACTIVITIES (on campus or nearby)
Field house facilities, golf, tennis, gymnasium.

AVAILABLE DATES
June 1 — August 10
Reservations are required.

CONTACT
Ray Cox
Business Manager
Telephone: (816) 248-3391

UNIVERSITY OF MISSOURI
Kansas City, Missouri 64110

Although separated by the Kansas River, Kansas City, Missouri, and Kansas City, Kansas, join to form a unique economic unit. A large trade center by virtue of grain and livestock markets, steel mills, petroleum refining and an important railroad depot, it forms a crossroads of central United States industrial marketing and distribution. Culture is important, too, and well represented by Philharmonic Orchestra and two noteworthy art museums.

ACCOMMODATIONS
Single room — $6.50 per person per day
Double room — $5.00 per person per day
Suite — $7.50 per person per day
Baths are shared. Pets and alcoholic beverages are not permitted.
Accommodations are available to students, alumni, adults, families and prospective matriculants.

MEALS
There is no set cost for meals. A cafeteria is available on campus.

ACTIVITIES (on campus or nearby)
Truman Library, the Plaza, Swope Park, and many museums.

AVAILABLE DATES
June 5 — July 25
Advance reservations are not required.

CONTACT
Mr. Van Miller
5030 Cherry Street
Telephone: (816) 276-1413

ROCKHURST COLLEGE
Kansas City, Missouri 64110

The college is situated in the cultural center of Kansas City — Westport — within walking distance of the Nelson Art Gallery, which is one of the greatest in the country. The area captures the spirit of pioneer days, and the River Quay evokes the city's past as the birthplace of rhythm and blues. Kansas City is a stroller's delight. It has almost as many miles of gracious boulevards as Paris and nearly equals the number of fountains and sculptures of Rome. The large Starlight Theatre features outdoor performances of various forms of entertainment, and the famous Kansas City Ballet Company, Philharmonic and Lyric Opera all have full and exciting seasons. Major league baseball is played in the city during the summer.

ACCOMMODATIONS
Single room — $8.00 per person per day;
$30.00 per person per week
Double room — $6.00 per person per day;
$20.00 per person per week.
Baths are shared. Linens are provided in the fee.
Pets are not permitted.
Accommodations are available to students, alumni, adults and prospective matriculants.

MEALS
There is a cafeteria and restaurant on campus and a nearby off-campus restaurant. Typical prices are not available.

ACTIVITIES (on campus or nearby)
The college is within walking distance of: Nelson Art Gallery, Atkins Museum, Conservatory of Music, Kansas City Art Institute, Museum Repertory Theatre, and Linda Hill Library (houses a tremendous scientific holding). The Midwest Research Institute is a few blocks away.

AVAILABLE DATES
June 1 — August 1
Reservations are required.

CONTACT
Kay L. Schippert, Assistant Dean of Students
Massman Hall, Rm. 7
Telephone: (816) 363-4010

WASHINGTON UNIVERSITY
St. Louis, Missouri

St. Louis is wealthy, handsome and urbane with myriad
attractions for the visitor. Don't miss: St. Louis Cardinal
baseball and football in Busch Stadium; Forest Park with
an outdoor Municipal Opera and the City Art Museum;
the historic riverfront; the Missouri Botannical Garden;
McDonnell Planetarium; Six Flags Over Mid-America.

ACCOMMODATIONS
Academic period:
Bunk room — $4.00 per person per day
Double room — $7.00 per person per day
Conference Period:
Single room — $8.00 per person per day
Double room — $6.00 per person per day
Non-Academic Period:
Single room — $7.00 per person per day
Double room — $4.00 per person per day
Bunk rooms have 4-6 bunk beds; can accommodate up to
12 persons. Pets are not permitted; no alcoholic beverages
in lounge areas of dorm, in Wohl Center, or in cafeterias.
Baths are shared or private, depending upon accommoda-
tion. Linens and maid service are included in the fee.
Accommodations are available during Academic Period to:
students, alumni, prospective matriculants, and friends,
relatives of current students, faculty or staff.
Accommodations are available during Non-Academic
Period to: general public, conference groups, students,
prospective matriculants.

MEALS
Cafeteria (typical prices)
Breakfast — $1.25
Lunch — $1.60
Dinner — $2.25

ACTIVITIES (on campus or nearby)
Indoor swimming and outdoor tennis on campus; no fee.
Fishing, boating, golf off-campus; fee charged.

AVAILABLE DATES
Limited guest housing during Academic Period —
August 15 — May 30; Unlimited guest housing during
Non-Academic Period — June 1 — August 14.
Reservations are strongly suggested.

CONTACT
Tootie Lewis, Coordinator, Conference & Guest Housing
6515 Wydown Blvd., Telephone: (314) 868-0010, ext. 4051

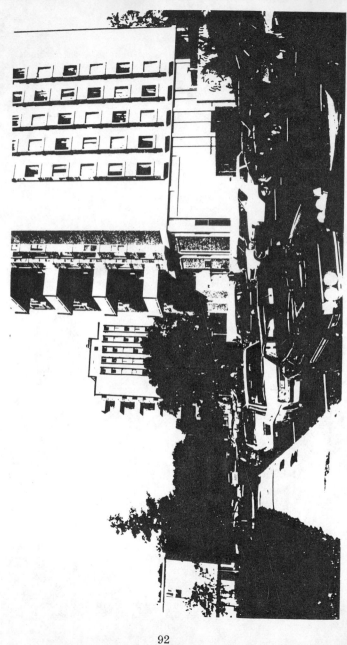

TARKIO COLLEGE
Tarkio, Missouri 64491

Tarkio is in northwest Missouri, midway between Kansas City and Omaha, Nebraska. This is a rich agricultural area, with rolling hills filled with cattle and corn. It's famous for its wildlife — deer, geese and turkey. The Rankin Mule Barn, listed in the National Registry of Historical Places, once served as the center of the David Rankin ranch empire. It now houses the college's Summer Theatre where, each summer, more than 11,000 people enjoy semi-professional performances of Broadway musicals. The college offers interesting, varied summer camps, workshops and institutes.

ACCOMMODATIONS
Single room — $7.00 per person per day;
$49.00 per person per week
Double room — $5.00 per person per day;
$35.00 per person per week
Apartment (accommodating 4) — $3.50 per person per day;
$24.50 per person per week
A cot in a room — $1.50 additional per night.
Pets are not permitted; no alcohol or illegal drugs on campus. Baths are shared. Linens are provided for a fee: $3.00 per week.
Accommodations are available to the general public.

MEALS
Cafeteria (typical prices)
Breakfast — $1.00
Lunch — $1.50
Dinner — $2.25
Cafeteria and snack bar on campus; restaurant off campus.

ACTIVITIES (on campus or nearby)
Swimming in an indoor pool and tennis: no charge.
Golf: $3.00 per day. Summer theatre: approximately $3.00 per person. Various summer campus, workshops and institutes.

AVAILABLE DATES
June 1 — August 15
Reservations are required.

CONTACT
Charles Sheppard
Vice President for Administrative Services
Rankin Hall
Telephone: (816) 736-4131

COLLEGE OF GREAT FALLS
Great Falls, Montana 59405

Definitely a town for the visitor interested in a restful,
outdoors-centered vacation. There is an 18 hole golf
course, three swimming facilities. At the Lewis and Clark
National Forest, you can enjoy acres and acres of canyons,
meadows, mountains, scenic drives, wilderness hikes,
stream and lake fishing, big-game hunting, picnicking,
winter sports, and camping. The flavor of Great Falls'
Western heritage comes alive during the State Fair in
late July with rodeos, horse races, nightly shows.

ACCOMMODATIONS
Single room — $5.00 per person per day;
$35.00 per person per week
Double room — $3.50 per person per day;
$24.50 per person per week
Apartment (accommodating up to 4 persons) — $3.50
per person per day, or, $8.00 per family per day
Baths are shared. Linens are provided at no cost.
Pets are not permitted.
Accommodations are available to general public.
Conventions can also be accommodated.

MEALS
Cafeteria (typical prices)
Breakfast — $1.00
Lunch — $1.25
Dinner — $2.00
Cafeteria and snack bar available on campus.

ACTIVITIES (on campus or nearby)
Swimming, fishing, hiking, boating, golf, tennis, water
skiing. All rental equipment available on campus.

AVAILABLE DATES
June 1 — August 15
Advance reservations required.

CONTACT
Mr. Leo Robertson
Housing Director
1301 Twentieth Street South
Telephone: (406) 761-8210, ext. 272

UNIVERSITY OF MONTANA
Missoula, Montana 59801

The Blackfoot and Bitterroot Rivers and Rock Creek
have played an important role in the development of
Missoula. First settled by Indians and hunters, the town
soon turned into an agrarian and industrial center.
Timber is also a part of Missoula's economy, and two
forestry services have their headquarters here. The city
is in western Montana, south of the Flathead Indian
Reservation, and near the Bitterroot Mountain Range.

ACCOMMODATIONS
Single room — $4.00 per person per day;
$21.00 per person per week
Double room — $3.00 per person per day;
$17.50 per person per week
Baths are shared. Maid service is $2.00 additional.
per day. Pets and children under 12 years of age are
not permitted.
Accommodations are available to students, alumni, adults
and prospective matriculants. Facilities are also available
for individuals who have some direct affiliation with the
university and with other university, community, civic
and religious organizations traveling in groups.

MEALS
Cafeteria (typical prices)
Breakfast — $1.45
Lunch — $1.85
Dinner — $2.75
A coffee shop is available.

ACTIVITIES (on campus or nearby)
Swimming, tennis, fishing and hiking. Nominal fees are
charged for rafting and backpacking equipment. Saint
Mary's Mission, Bitterroot Valley, Mission Valley and
Mountain Range, Bison Range, Glacier National Park and
Forts Missoula and Owen are within short distances.
Weekend trips and guided scenic tours may be arranged.

AVAILABLE DATES
June 15 — August 15
Advance reservations are required.

CONTACT
Mr. Ronald Brunell
Assistant Director, Residence Halls
Telephone: (406) 243-2611 or (406) 243-5321

NEBRASKA

CHADRON STATE COLLEGE
Chadron, Nebraska 60337

Chadron is in northwest Nebraska, close to the South
Dakota border. It is situated on cross-country Route 20
which connects to the major east-west turnpikes and
Route 26 to the west, leading to the Grand Teton and
Yellowstone National Parks in Wyoming. This central
U.S. plains state is strategically located for access to
mountains and lakes to the north, large farms to the east,
and cattle ranching to the west. Chadron was the starting
point of a historic 1,000 mile horse race to Chicago.
The winner took almost 14 days to complete the trip.

ACCOMMODATIONS
Single room — $3.00 per person per day;
$21.00 per person per week
Double room — $3.00 per person per day;
$21.00 per person per week
Baths are shared. Linens and maid service are included.
The charge per person per night is $2.50, excluding linen
service. Pets and alcoholic beverages are not permitted.
Accommodations are available to students, alumni, adults,
families and prospective matriculants.

MEALS
Cafeteria (typical prices)
Breakfast — $1.00
Lunch — $1.25
Dinner — $1.50
Banquets and private meals are available. Prices depend
upon menu desired. A coffee shop is available.

ACTIVITIES (on campus or nearby)
Swimming, fishing, tennis and hiking. There is a nominal
charge for swimming if desired at unscheduled hours.
The Black Hills are less than a one-hour drive away.
Fort Robinson, Museum of the Fur Trade, and Pine Ridge
area are nearby attractions. Fort Robinson also has a
summer theatre.

AVAILABLE DATES
June 3 — August 1 (for groups up to 300)
Facilities are available all year round for individuals
and smaller groups. Large groups may be accommodated
during the summer for conventions, reunions, etc. Groups
of up to 150 persons may be accommodated in the winter.

CONTACT
Mr. Donald J. Duncan
Telephone: (308) 432-4451, extension 230, 231, 232 and 233

KEARNEY STATE COLLEGE
Kearney, Nebraska

At one time, Kearney had hopes of being the state capital. Today, the city boasts a breath-taking countryside of farmland and forest. For an interesting side trip, visit the Harold Warp Pioneer Village with original sod house, pony express station, locomotives, and over a hundred antique autos. For the sports-minded, there is hunting, fishing, swimming, picnicking, and boating at Fort Kearney State Historical Park and Cottonmill Lake State Recreation Center. Kearney is a two-hour drive from Lincoln, the state capital, which has excellent shopping and cultural facilities; and a three-hour drive from Omaha, the home of Boys Town, founded by Father Flanagan in 1917.

ACCOMMODATIONS
Single room — $6.00 per person per day
Double room — $5.00 per person per day
Baths are shared. Linens are provided at no extra cost.
No pets are permitted.
Accommodations available to students, alumni, and prospective matriculants.

MEALS
Cafeteria (typical prices)
Breakfast — $1.50
Lunch — $1.90
Dinner — $2.50

AVAILABLE DATES
June 1 — August 20
Advance reservations are required.

CONTACT
Mr. Dan Duffy
Director of Housing
Telephone: (308) 236-4422

PERU STATE COLLEGE
Peru, Nebraska 68421

Peru is located in the hills along the Missouri River, in the southeastern corner of the state. It is near enough to Lincoln and Omaha to enjoy the influence of both cities' cultural and entertainment facilities. While in Lincoln, be sure to see the State Capitol — a handsome structure. Omaha, famous for Boys Town (founded by Father Flanagan in 1917), is also a midwestern educational leader with five colleges and universities in the city itself. Omaha also offers many recreation areas and parks with ample opportunities for hunting, fishing, picnicking, boating, camping, and swimming. There are cinemas, theatres, museums, and interesting shops. Take a car trip to historical Nebraska City and visit the Arbor Manor and John Brown's Cave.

ACCOMMODATIONS
Single room — $4.00 per person per day; $28.00 per person per week
Double room — $3.50 per person per day; $24.50 per person per week
Apartment (accommodating 4 persons) — $4.00 per person per day; $28.00 per person per week
Baths are private. Linens are provided for an additional fee of $1.00. Pets and alcoholic beverages are not permitted. Accommodations are available to the general public.

MEALS
Cafeteria (typical prices)
Breakfast — $ .95
Lunch — $1.25
Dinner — $1.50
Cafeteria and snack bar on campus. Restaurants off campus.

ACTIVITIES (on campus or nearby)
Tennis available on campus — no charge. Swimming and golf available in Auburn.

AVAILABLE DATES
Year round.
Advance reservations are required.

CONTACT
Mr. John D. Letts, Director of Housing
Box 192
Telephone: (402) 872-3815

CONCORDIA TEACHERS COLLEGE
Seward, Nebraska 68434

Seward is approximately 25 miles from Nebraska's capital,
Lincoln. The city is located on the Big Blue River in
Seward County. Omaha and Council Bluffs are 65 miles
to the northeast on the Missouri River. Corn, wheat,
cattle and sorghums are the major sources of income in
this Great Plains State.

ACCOMMODATIONS
Double room — $3.00 per person per day
Baths are shared. Linens and limited maid service
are included. Pets, smoking and alcoholic beverages
are not permitted.
Accommodations are available to students, alumni, adults,
families and prospective matriculants.

MEALS
There is no set cost for meals. A coffee shop and
cafeteria are available.

ACTIVITIES (on campus or nearby)
Swimming, tennis, bowling, baseball and boating.
Other attractions are art galleries, recreational facilities,
numerous lakes for fishing and water sports, and
nearby Lincoln capital building. A special event is
Seward's Fourth of July celebration.

AVAILABLE DATES
June 4 — August 16
Advance reservations are required.

CONTACT
Mr. Gilbert Heine
Director of College Relations
800 North Columbia Avenue
Telephone: (402) 643-3651, extension 221

NEVADA

UNIVERSITY OF NEVADA AT LAS VEGAS
Las Vegas, Nevada, 89109

On the campus is the Museum of Natural History, containing historic and prehistoric artifacts, live desert reptiles, and mining and pioneering artifacts. The Chemistry Building contains a display of 1,000 minerals. Also on campus is the Judy Bayley Theatre with year round performances. 31 miles northeast is Valley of Fire State Park, where the rock formations range from orange-pink to deep red. The rocks have been carved by the wind into strangely compelling shapes and the valley has petroglyphs, carved by prehistoric people, and petrified trees. The valley is an experience no visitor to Las Vegas should miss. A flight from McCarren Airport takes you to Grand Canyon for the day. There's day and night gambling at the casinos along the Strip, and spectacular nightclub shows.

ACCOMMODATIONS
$5.00 per person per day
Accommodations are available to students.

MEALS
Information is not available.

ACTIVITIES (on campus or nearby)
Off campus: water sports, skiing, golf, fishing, hunting, hiking, riding trails. Tours can be arranged.

AVAILABLE DATES
June 15 — August 15

CONTACT
Housing Office
1130 University Blvd.
Telephone: (702) 739-3469

UNIVERSITY OF NEVADA, RENO
Reno, Nevada 89507

Situated between hills to the east and the Sierras.
Reno is famed as a gambling and divorce center. It's also
a city of lovely houses, quiet streets, and beautiful
surroundings. The campus is on a plateau overlooking
the Sierra Nevada, the Virginia Mountains and the
Truckee Valley. It contains an historical museum with
pioneer artifacts, and prehistoric and modern Indian
collections. Also on campus is the Fleischmann
Atmospherium-Planetarium, where the 360° cameras
project remarkable displays on the dome. Tolyabe
National Forest, 10 miles west, provides big-game hunting,
saddle and pack trips, trout fishing, picnicking, and
winter sports. Lake Tahoe, Virginia City, Carson City,
and the Sierra Nevada are all within an hour's drive.

ACCOMMODATIONS
Rates are $4.00 per person per night.
Accommodations are available to supervised groups.

MEALS
Information is not available.

ACTIVITIES (on campus or nearby)
Off campus: deer and duck hunting, skiing, horseback
riding, sailing and boating, swimming, golf. On campus:
Winter Carnival in February.

AVAILABLE DATES
Year round
Reservations are suggested.

CONTACT
Housing Office
Box 8034, Union Station
Telephone: (702) 784-6107

UNIVERSITY OF NEW HAMPSHIRE
Durham, New Hampshire 03824

At the tip of Great Bay, just above Portsmouth, Durham offers a taste of New Hampshire's year-round recreational attractions. Twenty minutes due east is Maine; southeast, the Hampton and Rye beaches, with a day cruise to the Isle of Shoals. In the Durham area, there are three golf courses, horseback riding, tennis courts and woods for hiking. West and north are mountains and lake country. For theatre lovers, the University Summer Theatre offers a repertory program on-campus, while the Theatre of the Sea (in Portsmouth) and the Ogunquint Playhouse in Maine are nearby. Portsmouth offers many sightseeing and historic tours, particularly the Strawberry Banke.

ACCOMMODATIONS
Single room — $7.00 and $8.00 per person per day
Double room — $5.00 and $6.00 per person per day
Baths are shared. Pets, children under 6 years of age and alcoholic beverages (in areas other than the room) are not permitted.
Accommodations are available to students, alumni, adults and prospective matriculants.
University of New Hampshire also offers apartments for summer rental in Dover, New Hampshire. They contain two bedrooms, a living room, kitchen and bath and are furnished. Rental is $150 per month.

MEALS
A cafeteria is available.

ACTIVITIES (on campus or nearby)
The university offers tennis, swimming, boating and picnic facilities. Public facilities include golfing, riding and hiking. Canoe and camping equipment are available for rent.

AVAILABLE DATES
June 4 — August 23
Advance reservations are preferred.

CONTACT
Miss Gail Tufts
Residence Office, Stoke Hall
Telephone: (603) 862-2120

UPSALA COLLEGE
East Orange, New Jersey 07019

For lovers of horses and the hunt, East Orange is in the hub of activity. Suburban Essex County is a happy combination of rural and city life. Proximity to New York City is agreeable to commuters and accounts for a large portion of East Orange's population. The Hudson River is within short driving distance. Mountains and hills to the north and west provide nearby vacation areas.

ACCOMMODATIONS
Double room — $10.00 per person per day;
$60.00 per person per week
Baths are shared. Linens are included. Double rooms have single beds.
Accommodations are available to students, alumni, adults, families and prospective matriculants.

MEALS
A cafeteria is open for breakfast and lunch, a la carte.

ACTIVITIES (on campus or nearby)
Tennis courts, horseback riding, swimming, boating and fishing.

AVAILABLE DATES
June 15 — August 15

CONTACT
Residence Halls Office
Telephone: (201) 266-7234

KEAN COLLEGE OF NEW JERSEY
Union, New Jersey 07083

Union is in the cluster of New Jersey cities across the
river from New York City. It's about an hour's drive
from Asbury Park and Long Branch, part of the famed
resort beach front of New Jersey. There's swimming,
fishing (fresh water and ocean) and golf at both resorts.
Memorabilia of President Grover Cleveland are collected
at his birthplace in Caldwell, near Union. In Elizabeth,
east of Union, look for Boxwood Hall where Washington
stayed while on his way to his inauguration (1789).
Wasinanco Park, in Elizabeth, offers tennis, fishing,
boating and handsome gardens. Nearby Hackensack
contains one of the state's oldest churches, the Church
on the Green, and the interesting historical house,
Zabriskie-von Steuben House. Newark, where Stephen
Crane was born, has a remarkable group of sculptures
by Gutzon Borglum in Military Park. While here, visit
the Old Plume House, believed to have been built in
1710. The Morristown National Historical Park is a short
distance west of Union. The Continental Army bivouacked
here during the winters of 1777 and 1779-80.

ACCOMMODATIONS
Single room—$7.00 per person per day
Double room—$8.00 - $10.00 per day
Children will not be accommodated.
Accommodations are available to community, religious
and civic groups.

MEALS
Information is not available.

ACTIVITIES (on campus or nearby)
See description above.

AVAILABLE DATES
June 20—August 20
Reservations are required.

CONTACT
Housing Office
Morris Avenue
Telephone: (201) 527-2114

MONTCLAIR STATE COLLEGE
Upper Montclair, New Jersey 07043

Montclair is actually a suburb of New York City, as are many communities in the area. Many of the town's homes were built in the early twentieth century and the area has retained its varied architecture in more modern design.

ACCOMMODATIONS
Single room — $7.00 per person per day;
$49.00 per person per week to be paid in advance
Double room — $5.00 per person per day;
$35.00 per person per week to be paid in advance
Baths are shared. Maid service is $2.00 additional per day.
Pets, children under the age of 16, and illegal drugs
are not permitted.
Accommodations are available to students, alumni, adults, families and prospective matriculants.

MEALS
Cafeteria (typical prices)
Breakfast — $1.15
Lunch — $1.60
Dinner — $2.40
A coffee shop is available in the student center.

ACTIVITIES (on campus or nearby)
Swimming, tennis, and ball fields are available.
Nominal fees are charged. There is also a summer theatre. Trips and tours may be arranged.

AVAILABLE DATES
June 10 — August 10
Reservations must be made and paid for in advance.

CONTACT
Ms. Lois D. Redd
Housing Services, Bohn Hall
Normal Avenue
Telephone: (201) 893-5188

NEW MEXICO STATE UNIVERSITY, LAS CRUCES
Las Cruces, New Mexico 88001

Las Cruces is on the Rio Grande River, approximately
40 miles from the Mexican border and El Paso, Texas.
Several trails lead from Las Cruces to the mountains
east and west and to the fertile Mesilla Valley, a land
of beauty and vast agricultural and mineral resources.
This region has been developed by the Elephant Butte
Dam, one of the government's greatest irrigation projects.
Folklore of the area includes Emperor Maximilian and
Billy the Kid. The 6,250-acre campus is one of the largest
in the world. A vast construction program by the university
is developing some of the most impressive facilities.

ACCOMMODATIONS
Pets, children under 12 years of age and alcoholic
beverages are not permitted.
Accommodations are available for students, adults,
and prospective matriculants.

MEALS
A cafeteria and coffee shop are on campus.

ACTIVITIES (on campus or nearby)
Swimming, fishing, tennis, hiking, golf and natatorium —
handball. Nominal fees are charged for swimming, golf,
and tennis. Some family picnics, weekend trips, and
guided scenic tours are organized by the Short Course
Director. Scenic recreational, historic and cultural
attractions include mountains, Mesilla Valley,
plays, concerts and art shows.

AVAILABLE DATES
Facilities are available year round if there is space
in the residence halls.
Advance reservations are required.

CONTACT
Mr. Anthony Valach
Director of Housing
Regents Row Residence Center, Housing Department
Telephone: (505) 646-3202

NEW MEXICO INSTITUTE OF TECHNOLOGY
Socorro, New Mexico 87801

Socorro is on the Rio Grande River, bordered by
mountains on three sides and a mesa on the fourth.
The fertile river valley is excellent livestock and cotton
producing land, the town's major sources of income.
As the Southwestern states were once rich in silver and
zinc, Socorro operates a State Bureau of Mines and
Mineral Resources. The San Miguel Franciscan Mission,
originated in 1598, is an interesting tourist attraction.
During the silver mining boom, Socorro flourished as the
largest city in New Mexico and boasted 44 saloons
on its main street.

ACCOMMODATIONS
Single room — $3.00 per person per day;
$21.00 per person per week
Double room — $1.50 per person per day;
$10.50 per person per week
Baths are shared. Linen service is an additional 75¢.
Alcoholic beverages are not permitted. Accommodations
are available to students, alumni, adults and prospective
matriculants.

MEALS
Cafeteria (typical prices)
Breakfast — $1.25
Lunch — $1.60
Dinner — $1.95
A coffee shop is available.

ACTIVITIES (on campus or nearby)
Tennis, golf, swimming, backpacking, rodeos, mountain
climbing and water sports.

AVAILABLE DATES
May 15 — August 15
December 15 — January 15
Advance reservations are required.

CONTACT
Mr. Kurt G. Krammer
Office of Student Affairs
Campus Station
Telephone: (505) 835-5208

NEW YORK

STATE UNIVERSITY OF NEW YORK
Agricultural and Technical College
Alfred, New York 14802

Alfred is a host town to the rapidly expanding educational system of the State University of New York. An important ceramics and porcelain collection is exhibited on the Alfred campus. The nearest Finger Lake is a half-hour drive to the northeast; Rochester is about 65 miles north.

ACCOMMODATIONS
Single room — $4.00 per person per day;
$14.00 per person per week
Double room — $4.00 per person per day;
$21.00 per person per week
Baths are shared. Linens are $1.00 additional. Maid service is provided. Pets are not permitted.
Accommodations are available to students, alumni, adults, families and prospective matriculants.

MEALS
The average cost of meals is $5.00 to $6.00 per day.
A cafeteria and coffee shop are available.

ACTIVITIES (on campus or nearby)
An Olympic-sized swimming pool, ten tennis courts, and golf facilities are available. Corning Glass Center, summer theatre, Finger Lakes parks, Niagara Falls, Fort Niagara, Letchworth Park, and wineries are nearby. Guided scenic tours and weekend trips may be arranged.

AVAILABLE DATES
July 1 — August 15
Advance reservations are preferred.

CONTACT
Mr. Reed D. Lowrey
Director, Continuing Education
3 North Hall
Telephone: (607) 871-6101

BARD COLLEGE
Annandale-on-Hudson, New York 12504

The 550-acre campus, bordering on the Hudson River, is just fifteen miles from historic Hyde Park. Here you can visit the Home of Franklin D. Roosevelt National Historic Site, where the President was born and where he and his wife, Anna Eleanor Roosevelt, are buried in the rose garden. Just one mile north is the Vanderbilt Mansion National Historic Site, a wonderful example of the American Palace era. There's a good summer theatre in Hyde Park. Four miles north of Hyde Park is the Ogden Mills and Ruth Livingston Memorial State Park with a French Renaissance mansion and facilities for boating, picnicking, and golf. Fishing, picnicking and a cafe are available at the Margaret Lewis Norrie State Park, 3 miles north of Annandale. Several hundred examples of Frederick J. Waugh's marine drawings and paintings are housed in the nearby Edwin E. Ulrich Art Museum.

ACCOMMODATIONS
The facilities include single rooms and a few suites of 3 rooms, suitable for families. Rates not established at time of printing; check for further information. Pets are not permitted. Baths are shared except in the suites.
Accommodations are available to the general public and organized groups.

MEALS
Groups of 50-100 — inquire for fees.
No meals are served on campus except to groups.
A snack bar and restaurant are nearby, off-campus.

ACTIVITIES (on campus or nearby)
Off campus: hiking; picnicking; golf; boating; fishing (see description above).

AVAILABLE DATES
January. June 1 — August 31
Reservations are required.

CONTACT
William M. Asip
Business Manager, Business Office
Telephone: (914) 758-6822

CONCORDIA COLLEGE
Bronxville, New York 10708

Bronxville, between White Plains and Yonkers, is on
the New York City line. The area is filled with lovely
homes and historical restorations. The Philipse Manor
Hall, in Yonkers, was the home of Dutch manor lords
until 1779, and shouldn't be missed. There's harness racing
nearby at Yonkers Raceway. Washington Irving's home,
Sunnyside, a singular, charming melange of architecture
in Tarrytown, contains the author's library, furniture
and personal effects. Van Cortlandt Manor, in Croton-on-
Hudson, is a beautiful estate built circa 1749. In North
Tarrytown is an early 1700's gristmill-trading-manor
complex, Philipsburg Manor, which has been restored
and furnished in all its 1720's baronial splendor.
South of Bronxville is the Bronx, a borough of New York
City. Don't miss: Yankee Stadium for baseball; the famed
Bronx Zoo and Botanical Gardens; Valentine-Varien
House Museum, scene of a Revolutionary War skirmish;
Poe Cottage, where the poet lived in 1846-49; Wave Hill
Center for Environmental Studies.

ACCOMMODATIONS
Fees range from $5.00 - $7.00.
Accommodations are available to the general public.

MEALS
Information is not available.

ACTIVITIES (on campus or nearby)
Sightseeing (see description above); golf and harness
racing in Yonkers.

AVAILABLE DATES
May 25 — August 25
Reservations are required.

CONTACT
Housing Office
Telephone: (914) 337-9300

CANISIUS COLLEGE
Buffalo, New York 14208

The campus is located on Buffalo's main street, five minutes away from the downtown area. Buffalo, modeled after Washington, D.C., radiates from Niagara Square with its monument to President William McKinley who was assassinated here in 1901. The city has 3,000 acres of park where you can ride, swim, boat and play golf and tennis. Take the Skyway Drive for a good view of the city and harbor. There are several municipal pools for summer swimming and four municipal golf courses. There's a children's park in Fantasy Island, as well as rides, shows, an animated garden, cafes and a saloon, plus picnic facilities. There's a three-hour cruise of the harbor, Niagara River and Lake Erie every day during the summer. The campus is just a 30 minute drive from Niagara Falls. Don't miss Old Fort George and Old Fort Niagara while there.

ACCOMMODATIONS
Single room — $5.00 per person per day;
$22.00 per person per week
Double room — $4.00 per person per day;
$17.00 per person per week
Pets are not permitted. Baths are shared. Linens and maid service are included in the fee.
Accommodations are available to students; alumni; adults; families; small children; prospective matriculants; any guest of someone at the college or anyone with a connection to the college.

MEALS
Cafeteria (typical prices)
Breakfast — $1.00
Lunch — $1.25
Dinner — $1.65
Open weekdays. There is a nearby restaurant, off-campus.

ACTIVITIES (on campus or nearby)
Golf at Delaware Park course, 10 minutes away: $2.50-$3.50 per round. Tennis, at city courts, about 10 minutes away; no fee.

AVAILABLE DATES
Year round.
Reservations are required.

CONTACT
John B. Crabbe, Director of Residence Life
Bosch Hall, 2001 Main Street
Telephone: (716) 883-7000

NEW YORK UNIVERSITY COLLEGE
Geneseo, New York 14454

Geneseo, located in the northwestern section of New York, about 30 miles south of Rochester, lies in lovely rolling farm country. There's a good county fair in mid-July, and an Indian ceremony re-enactment on Labor Day weekend, at Canandaigua, which is about 30 miles east of Geneseo. Rochester, on the Genesee River near Lake Ontario, is worth a full day's tour from Geneseo. While here, tour the Eastman Kodak plant and see some of the city's most famous sites: Museum and Science Center; Xerox Biology Exhibit; Seneca Park Zoo; Campbell-Whittlesey House, a handsome Greek Revival mansion. Niagara Falls and Buffalo are about 1½ hours drive from Geneseo.

ACCOMMODATIONS
Fees range from $2.00 - $5.00
Accommodations are available to male students.

MEALS
Information is not available.

ACTIVITIES (on campus or nearby)
Fishing, golf, touring in vicinity. Racing at Finger Lakes Race Track (about 40 miles east of Geneseo).

AVAILABLE DATES
Year round

CONTACT
Housing Office
129 Main Street
Telephone: (716) 243-9760

HOUGHTON COLLEGE
Houghton, New York 14744

Houghton is an Alleghany County village in the northern tier of New York State—in an area noted for its scenic interest. The town is on the Genesee River, 65 miles from Niagara Falls, 35 miles from Rock City, and 15 miles from Letchworth State Park. Surrounding the campus are rolling hills, rich in Indian and colonial lore.

ACCOMMODATIONS
Single room—$7.00 per person per day
Double room—$3.50 per person per day
Baths are shared. Linens are provided. Pets, smoking and alcoholic beverages are not permitted.
Accommodations are available to students, alumni, adults, families and prospective matriculants.

MEALS
Cafeteria (typical prices)
Breakfast — $1.00
Lunch — $1.50
Dinner — $2.50
A coffee shop is available.

ACTIVITIES (on campus or nearby)
Hiking, tennis, golf and swimming.

AVAILABLE DATES
June 15—August 15
Advance reservations are required.

CONTACT
Mr. Kenneth L. Nielsen
Business Manager
    or
Barbara A. Hora
Conference Coordinator
Telephone: (716) 567-2211, extension 118

KEUKA COLLEGE
Keuka Park, New York 14478

Keuka College is located in Keuka Park on Keuka Lake
in the heart of the lovely Finger Lake Region. The 173-
acre campus is one hour's drive from Syracuse, Rochester
and Elmira and is easily reached via the New York
Thruway. The world famous Corning Glass Center in
Corning, housing exhibits of man-made glass from 1500
B.C. and demonstrations of modern glass-making, is an
hour away by car. Equally close is Watkins Glen, a
breathtaking vista of cataracts, rapids and gorge where
you can swim, climb and picnic. Don't miss Syracuse's
Canal Museum which contains an interesting collection
of canal history and memorabilia; Rochester's Museum
& Science Center; Mark Twain Study, in Elmira, built
in the shape of a riverboat pilothouse, where Twain wrote
many of his stories.

ACCOMMODATIONS
Single room — $8.00 per person per day
Double room — $6.00 per person per day
Baths are shared. Linens are provided: $2.00. Pets
are not permitted.
Accommodations are available to students, alumni, adults,
families, prospective matriculants and conference groups.
Rates for conferences are available on request.

MEALS
Cafeteria (typical prices)
Breakfast — $1.00
Lunch — $2.50
Dinner — $3.00
Cafeteria on campus; closed from mid-November
through first week of January, and late August.
A snack bar and restaurant are nearby.

ACTIVITIES (on campus or nearby)
Swimming, boating, hiking, tennis, fishing, golf are on
campus or nearby. For information on the Finger Lake
Region, write the Finger Lakes Association, Dept. K,
309 Lake St., Penn Yan, New York 14527.

AVAILABLE DATES
Year round.
Reservations are required.

CONTACT
Miss Suzanne R. Goodrich
Director of Conference and Custodial Services
Telephone: (315) 536-4411

MANHATTAN COLLEGE
Bronx, New York 10471

New York City. To millions, it is the center of the world.
Business and commerce, the theatre, communications arts,
almost every major activity of modern life are identified
by generic locations. Wall Street. Broadway. Fifth Avenue.
The Garment Center. Radio City and Rockefeller Center.
The Empire State Building. Madison Avenue. The
Verrazano Bridge with its breath-taking view of New York
Harbor, one of the world's busiest ports. It would take
a lifetime and more to take it all in. But one fare can
let the visitor travel 256 miles on its public transportation
system — through the five boroughs of Bronx, Manhattan,
Brooklyn, Queens and Staten Island.

ACCOMMODATIONS
Single room — $7.00 per person per day;
$49.00 per person per week
Double room — $5.00 per person per day;
$35.00 per person per week
Apartment — $5.00 per person per day (groups only)
Baths are shared for room accommodations and private
for apartments. Pets are not permitted.
Accommodations are available to students, prospective
matriculants and educational groups.

MEALS
Cafeteria (typical prices)
Breakfast — $1.25
Lunch — $2.50
Dinner — $4.00
Special meal arrangements are available for groups.

ACTIVITIES (on campus or nearby)
Public facilities include golf, tennis and swimming.
New York City Summer Programs available.

AVAILABLE DATES
May 25 — August 25
Advance reservations are required for groups only.

CONTACT
Mr. Richard C. Kemp or Ms. Mary Barrett, Ext. 379
Director of Residence
4513 Manhattan College Parkway
Telephone: (212) 548-1400, extension 438

WAGNER COLLEGE
Staten Island, New York 10301

Wagner College is in New York City's borough of
Richmond, overlooking the busy New York harbor and the
Manhattan skyline. An unforgettable 20-minute ride on
the Staten Island Ferry puts you at the foot of the
empire city. Staten Island Institute of Arts and Sciences,
zoo and the restored colonial village are on the top of
the list of sites to see. The breathtaking Verrazano-
Narrows Bridge, the longest suspension bridge in the
world, connects Staten Island and Brooklyn.

ACCOMMODATIONS
Double room — $8.00 per person per day;
$50.00 per person per week
Baths are shared. Pets are not permitted.
Accommodations are available to students, alumni, adults,
families and prospective matriculants.

MEALS
Cafeteria (typical prices)
Breakfast — $1.45
Lunch — $2.50
Dinner — $3.35
A coffee shop is available.

ACTIVITIES (on campus or nearby)
Golf, horseback riding, concerts in the park.

AVAILABLE DATES
May 22 — August 2
Limited accommodations through August 16.
Advance reservations are required.

CONTACT
Dr. William A. Rowen
631 Howard Avenue
Telephone: (212) 390-3270

PACE UNIVERSITY—WESTCHESTER
Pleasantville, New York 10570

Pleasantville is a picturesque community 35 miles north
of New York City, the country's largest metropolis and
undisputed cultural center. Its rolling hills offer many
outdoor attractions. The town is the site of one of the
world's largest publishing organizations.

ACCOMMODATIONS
Single room—$7.50 per person per day;
$35.00 per person per week
Double room—$7.50 per person per day;
$35.00 per person per week
Baths are shared. Cribs are not available. Pets are
not permitted.
Accommodations are available to students, alumni, adults,
families and prospective matriculants.

MEALS
A cafeteria is available.

ACTIVITIES (on campus or nearby)
Tennis, ping pong, arcade games, golf and a
gymnasium. New York City tour buses are available.
Picnic areas are located in various Westchester parks.
Archery equipment is available. White Plains Concert
Series is active during the summer. The Phillips
Manor House, the Old Mill in Tarrytown (a storied
Hudson River village), and the Kensico Dam and Park
are nearby attractions.

AVAILABLE DATES
June 1—August 15
Advance reservations are required.

CONTACT
Mr. William Andreorio
Housing Office, Men's Dormitory
861 Bedford Road
Telephone: (914) 769-3200, extension 275

EISENHOWER COLLEGE
Senaca Falls, New York 13148

Senaca Falls was the site of the first convention of the
U.S. Women's Suffrage Movement in 1848. Three major
figures in the movement—Elizabeth Cady Stanton,
Susan B. Anthony and Amelia Jenks Bloomer (who gave
her name to this female garment) —were active in the
city. The Historical Museum contains memorabilia of
the Movement as well as other exhibits. The #2 and #3
Barge Canal Locks may be viewed from an observation
platform off East Bayard Street. Cayuka Lake provides
swimming, boating, fishing and picnicking. The Montezuma
National Wildlife Refuge, about 5 miles away, is a
sanctuary for wild fowl. Nearby Geneva, on Seneca
Lake, is known as the "fisherman's paradise." It's also
notable for the Rose Hill Mansion (a Greek Revival
mansion), Dahlia Gardens, and the Historical Museum.
The lake has a marina and provisions for camping,
picnicking, fishing and swimming.

ACCOMMODATIONS
Single room—$6.00 - $9.00 per person per day
Accommodations are available to community, religious
and civic groups.

MEALS
Information is not available.

ACTIVITIES (on campus or nearby)
Off-campus: tennis, fishing, boating, swimming.

AVAILABLE DATES
June 1—August 15

CONTACT
Housing Office
Telephone: (315) 568-7211

RUSSELL SAGE COLLEGE
Troy, New York 12180

Just north of Troy is Grandma Moses Schoolhouse, a one-room structure where the great primitive artist and her descendants were educated and where some of her memorabilia and family possessions are displayed. The house where she died, at the age of 101, is nearby. Within Troy is a fine 1827 sandstone Federal mansion, the Historical Society building, with period rooms and changing exhibits. Schenectady, about ½-hour's drive from Troy, has lovely old 18th century houses, particularly in the Village-Stockade Area which visitors may tour on foot. There are planetarium shows as well as science and art exhibits at the Schenectady Museum. Albany is a near neighbor of Troy. It is the capital of the state and still operates under its original charter, granted in 1686. Albany has two notable churches which should not be missed: First Church in Albany (Reformed) with a handsome hourglass pulpit, and St. Peter's Episcopal Church with beautiful stained glass windows.

ACCOMMODATIONS
Single room — $11.50 per person per day
Double room — $9.50 per person per day
Prices are approximate.
Smoking in the rooms, and pets, are not permitted.
Baths are shared. Linens are provided.
Accommodations are available to conferences and groups.

MEALS
$10.00 total per person per day

ACTIVITIES (on campus or nearby)
Theatres and tennis courts (no fee) on campus. Day trips to Lake George, Tanglewood and the Berkshires.
Saratoga Performing Arts Center is 25 miles away.
Hiking, etc.

AVAILABLE DATES
Last week in May — 3rd week in August
Reservations are required.

CONTACT
Ronald Schongar
Director, Summer Conferences
47 Ferry Street
Telephone: (518) 270-2201

MOHAWK VALLEY COMMUNITY COLLEGE
Utica, New York 13501

On the Mohawk River between Rome and Mohawk, the then village of Utica was an important trading center on the stagecoach route from Albany in the late 1900's. Now a highly industrial city, Utica offers every winter sport, the Upstate Auto Museum, and other historical and arts showings. Nearby are New York's picturesque Genesee Valley and Finger Lakes.

ACCOMMODATIONS
Single room — $8.50 per person for 1st night ($2.50 for each additional night up to 6 nights);
$20.50 per person per week
Double room — $7.50 per person for 1st night ($2.50 for each additional night up to 6 nights);
$18.50 per person per week
Suits (accommodates 7) — same rates as double room.
Accommodations can be made for groups up to 160 persons. Baths are shared. Linens provided: 3 towels, 2 sheets, 1 pillowcase per person per week. Blanket and pillow are $2.00 additional. Pets and alcoholic beverages (except beer and wine) are not permitted.
Accommodations are available to the general public.

MEALS
Cafeteria (typical prices)
Breakfast — $1.00
Lunch — $1.56
Dinner — $1.75
A coffee shop is available. A la carte items also available

ACTIVITIES (on campus or nearby)
Tennis, golf, hiking, swimming, backpacking, historic landmarks and skiing.

AVAILABLE DATES
June 1 — August 15
Advance reservations are required. Must be checked in no later than 6:00 P.M.

CONTACT
Mr. Robert Metzger
Director of Residence Halls, Dorm II
Telephone: (315) 792-5371

EAGLES NEST CONFERENCE CAMPUS —
MOUNT OLIVE COLLEGE
Mt. Olive, North Carolina 28365

One of the oldest towns in the state, New Bern, is a one-hour drive from Mt. Olive, and is famous for its scenic old buildings and historical sites and markers. Don't miss the Tyron Palace Restoration, the colonial capitol of North Carolina and a singularly lovely building and grounds. It has been completely furnished with period antiques. Drive due northwest for one hour from Mt. Olive to Raleigh, the present state capitol. Here you will find a unique blend of the old and new — beautifully restored antebellum homes mixed in with the modern commercial and merchandising structures. Enjoy all the cultural advantages of a modern, bustling city in the tradition of southern hospitality.

ACCOMMODATIONS
Single room — $5.00 per person per day;
$20.00 per person per week
Double room — $5.00 per person per day;
$25.00 per person per week
Camping facilities — $3.00 per night
Baths are shared. Pets are not permitted. Cots available for $1.00 additional.
Accommodations are available to the general public, students, alumni, adults.

MEALS
Cafeteria (typical prices)
Breakfast — $1.00
Lunch — $1.60
Dinner — $1.60

ACTIVITIES (on campus or nearby)
Swimming, fishing, hiking, boating, tennis available on campus. Canoes and sailboats may be obtained at no extra cost.

AVAILABLE DATES
Summer only. Advance reservations are required.

CONTACT
Mr. Charles Harrell
Business Manager
Telephone: (919) 658-4933

MOUNT OLIVE COLLEGE
Mount Olive, North Carolina 28365

Mount Olive, deep in the tobacco growing region of the South, is approximately 60 miles from Raleigh, the capital city of North Carolina. The Cape Fear River in Mount Olive and the Neuse River to the south, provide the town with a variety of water sports and fishing. Pamlico Sound and the shore are an approximate 1½-hour drive from Mount Olive.

ACCOMMODATIONS
Single room — $3.00 per person per day;
$21.00 per person per week
Double room — $5.00 per person per day;
$17.00 per person per week
Pets and alcoholic beverages are not permitted.
Maid service is provided and baths are shared.
Accommodations are available to students, alumni, adults, families and prospective matriculants.

MEALS
Cafeteria (typical prices)
Breakfast — $1.00
Lunch — $1.60
Dinner — $1.60
A coffee shop is available.

ACTIVITIES (on campus or nearby)
State park, tennis, camping, swimming and water sports. No fees are charged for these activities. Canoes are available for rental.

AVAILABLE DATES
June 15 — August 15
December 15 — January 15
Advance reservations are required.

CONTACT
Mr. Charles H. Harrell
P.O. Box 151
Telephone: (919) 658-4933

WARREN WILSON COLLEGE
Swannanoa, North Carolina 28778

Set in the beautiful Blue Ridge Mountains, Swannanoa
is just 8 miles east of Asheville. Asheville, a famous
resort is divided into three sections by the Swannanoa
and French Broad Rivers. It holds one of the best of the
craftsmen's fairs in the south, in July. The old handicraft
methods are still used and demonstrated here at the
Biltmore Industries Village. Here too are Old World
shops and an Antique Automobile Museum. Next to the
Village is the Biltmore House and Gardens. This is a
prime example of American Palace architecture, built
by George W. Vanderbilt at the turn of the century on a
12,000-acre estate. The house itself covers four acres,
and contains a famous collection of art, including original
Sargents and Boldinis. Thomas Wolfe's birthplace,
recognizable as "Dixieland" in *Look Homeward Angel*,
is finished with family possessions. 25 miles southeast is
famous Chimney Rock, a giant granite outcropping which
rises 315 feet. You can either climb to its peak or ride
up in the elevator built inside the ciff beside the chimney.

ACCOMMODATIONS
Single room—$5.00 per person per day
Double room—$5.00 per person per day
Children under 6 are free.
No alcohol in dormitories. Pets and illegal drugs are
not permitted. Wine and beer are sold in the cafeteria.
Baths are shared. Bedding is provided.
Accommodations are available, on a limited basis, to the
general public; conferences (of non-profit affiliated
groups) up to 100 persons.

MEALS
Cafeteria (typical prices)
Breakfast — $1.00
Lunch — $1.25
Dinner — $1.55 (Steak Night — $1.65

ACTIVITIES (on campus or nearby)
On campus: swimming pond; tennis courts when not in
use by students. Prehistoric Indian digs are on campus.

AVAILABLE DATES
June 1—July 31
Reservations are required.

CONTACT
Walter H. Kreamer
Business Manager
Telephone: (704) 298-3325

JAMESTOWN COLLEGE
Jamestown, North Dakota 56401

Jamestown lies in the fertile valley of the winding James
River in the southeastern part of North Dakota, along
Interstate 94. The Jamestown Dam just north of the city
has created a large recreational area. Arrowwood National
Wildlife Refuge, north of Jamestown, is a nesting and
feeding ground for ducks, geese, swans, gulls, pelicans,
terns and other birds.

ACCOMMODATIONS
Double room — $8.00 per person per day;
$50.00 per person per week
Suites — $12.00 for four or more persons per day;
Suites accommodate four or more persons and consist
of three rooms with private bath — available for families.
Baths are shared. Linens are supplied.
Accommodations are available to students, alumni,
prospective matriculants and groups.

MEALS
Cafeteria (typical prices)
Breakfast — $1.00
Lunch — $1.50
Dinner — $1.75

ACTIVITIES (on campus or nearby)
Boating and fishing on nearby Jamestown Reservoir;
tennis, indoor swimming pool on campus; game refuges
with 180 species of waterfowl on one of America's finest
migratory flyways.

AVAILABLE DATES
June 1 — September 1

CONTACT
Mr. Lloyd Peterson
Director of Business Affairs
Telephone: (701) 252-4331, extension 214

MAYVILLE STATE COLLEGE
Mayville, North Dakota 58257

Mayville is on the Goose River in the eastern section of
North Dakota, midway between Grand Forks and Fargo.
You can picnic, swim and play tennis in nearby Woodland
Park in Hillsboro. Grand Forks, about 40 miles away,
is at the fork of the Red River of the North and the
Red Lake River. It was a trading post for French fur
trappers, then a frontier river town. The city holds stock
car races on Fridays during the summer. While here,
visit the University of North Dakota to see the steel-
gridded sphere, the "Eternal Flame of Knowledge," and
the Oriental tapestries housed in the library. Fargo, the
state's largest city, is in the rich Red River Valley.
While here, visit Forsberg House which contains pioneer-
through-Victorian period furniture and memorabilia.

ACCOMMODATIONS
Single room — $5.00 per person per day
Double room — $10.00 per day
Accommodations are available to students. Length of
stay: 7-day maximum.

MEALS
Information is not available.

ACTIVITIES (on campus or nearby)
Off campus: swimming, boating, water sports.
Golf available in Grand Forks and Fargo.

AVAILABLE DATES
June 1 — August 10
Reservations are required.

CONTACT
Housing Officer
Telephone: (701) 786-2301

OHIO UNIVERSITY
Athens, Ohio 45701

OHIO

The University is the oldest college in what was once the Northwest Territory. William Holmes McGuffey, editor of the *McGuffey Readers*, was its president from 1839-1843. Lake Hope, in the Zaleski State Forest, has scenic trails, boating and swimming. There is fishing, swimming, picnicking and boating at Strouds Run and Burr Oak. Sections of Wayne National Forest are nearby. About 70 miles away, another section of the forest contains Lake Vesuvius. Here, the stack of one of the earliest iron blast furnaces, built in 1833, still remains.

ACCOMMODATIONS
Single room — $4.00 per person per day
Children are not accommodated.
Accommodations are available to adults.

MEALS
Information is not available.

ACTIVITIES (on campus or nearby)
On campus: summer theatre performances (late June-mid August), campus tours. Off campus: hiking, boating, swimming and fishing at nearby parks.

AVAILABLE DATES
Year round
Reservations are required.

CONTACT
Housing Office
Chubb Hall
Telephone: (614) 594-5151

BALDWIN-WALLACE COLLEGE
Berea, Ohio 44017

Berea is about 15 miles from Cleveland's center.
Cleveland is the largest city in the state with a varied
ethnic background. Its settlers came from Greece,
Lithuania, Germany, Italy, Poland, Yugoslavia, Ireland
and Russia. It's the home of an internationally famous
orchestra and four professional sports teams. In the
downtown area, visit "The Mall" which contains
government and municipal buildings surrounding a plaza,
and Cleveland Stadium, home of the Indians and Browns
teams. A good view of the city is obtained at Terminal
Tower. On the West Side, visit the Lake Erie Junior
Nature & Science Center (live animals and planetarium),
and the zoo, which is particularly interesting for children.
The nearby Oldest Stone House has herb and old-fashioned
gardens, and early 19th century furnishings. The East
Side offers Dunham Tavern Museum, a restoration of a
stagecoach inn, and an interesting Health Museum.
There's an aquarium in Gordon Park and Jewish art
and ceremonial objects at the Temple Museum, all in
the University Circle area.

ACCOMMODATIONS
Single room — $8.00 - $10.00 per person per night
Accommodations are available to the general public.

MEALS
Information is not available.

ACTIVITIES (on campus or nearby)
Sightseeing tours of Cleveland. Cuyahoga County Fair
in Berea in August. Summer Pops concerts by the
Cleveland Orchestra (Blossom Music Center).
Musicarnival (musical comedies in-the-round) from
mid-June to early September, in Cleveland.

AVAILABLE DATES
June 20 — August 31
Reservations are required.

CONTACT
Housing Officer
Telephone: (216) 826-2900

BLUFFTON COLLEGE
Bluffton, Ohio 45817

Bluffton is located midway between Lima and Findlay
on Interstate 75. Now typical of Ohio's industrial and
agricultural economy, this area was formerly one of the
nation's richest petroleum producers. In the late 1880's
and early 1890's, many wells yielding gas and oil were
opened and brought excitement to the entire region.
The 215-acre campus founded by the Mennonite Church
is partly covered with a natural forest of oak, elm, beech,
maple and more than 100 other varieties of trees. The
Riley Creek flows through the eastern side of the campus.

ACCOMMODATIONS
Double room — $4.00 per person per day;
$28.00 per person per week
Baths are shared. Pets, smoking, and alcoholic beverages
are not permitted.
Accommodations are available to students, alumni, adults,
families and prospective matriculants.

MEALS
Cafeteria (typical prices)
Breakfast — $ .75
Lunch — $1.10
Dinner — $1.60

ACTIVITIES (on campus or nearby)
Tennis, swimming, hiking, table tennis, billiards, bicycling
and picnicking. Equipment is available for rent.
The Antique Car Show is June 15-16.

AVAILABLE DATES
June 1 — August 15
Reservations are required one week in advance.

CONTACT
Mr. Frederick Amstutz
Telephone: (419) 358-8015, extension 240

UNIVERSITY OF CINCINNATI
Cincinnati, Ohio 45221

OHIO

Founded in 1788, Longfellow called Cincinnati "the Queen City of the West" and Charles Dickens remarked that it is "a place that commends itself ... favorably and pleasantly to a stranger." And it certainly has many favorable and pleasant things to see. If you enjoy museums Cincinnati offers a wide variety: Cincinnati Art Museum, Museum of Natural History, Fire Department Historical Museum, Taft Museum and Stowe House State Memorial. For recreation be sure to visit the Airport Playfield and Kings Island Amusement Park, and Cincinnati Zoological Gardens. Not to be overlooked is the fact that Cincinnati houses two of the country's finest restaurants: the Gourmet with its German-European decor and the Maisonette, which is reputed to have excellent French cuisine.

ACCOMMODATIONS
Single room — $7.00 per person per day
Double room — $5.00 per person per day
Baths are shared. Linens and maid service are provided.
Pets are not permitted.
Accommodations are available to groups attending workshops, institutes, conferences and conventions.

MEALS
Cafeteria (typical prices)
Breakfast — $ .95
Lunch — $1.45
Dinner — $2.20

ACTIVITIES (on campus or nearby)
None available on campus. Nearby — Cincinnati!

AVAILABLE DATES
June 20 — August 31, 1975
Advance reservations are required.

CONTACT
Marion D. Haisley
Director, Campus Calendar Office
320 Tangeman
University Center
Telephone: (513) 475-2442

XAVIER UNIVERSITY
Cincinnati, Ohio 45207

Cincinnati has grown from an early settlement in the
basin of the Ohio River to the second largest city in Ohio,
the possessor of a symphony orchestra, several distinguished art museums and two universities. The world's
largest inland coal port, it is the bituminous coal center
of the United States. Its proximity to Indiana and
Kentucky has made it a market center, as well as
attracting travelers to enjoy the numerous recreational
and cultural advantages of Cincinnati.

ACCOMMODATIONS
Single room — $4.00 per person per day;
$21.00 per person per week
Double room — $4.00 per person per day;
$21.00 per person per week
All rooms are in suites. Baths are private. Pets are not
permitted. Accommodations are available to students,
alumni, adults, families and prospective matriculants.

MEALS
Cafeteria (typical prices)
Breakfast — $1.10
Lunch — $1.40
Dinner — $1.80
A coffee shop is available.

ACTIVITIES (on campus or nearby)
Tennis, basketball, water sports, golf and theatre.

AVAILABLE DATES
Facilities are available all year round.
Advance reservations are required.

CONTACT
Mr. David A. Tom
Victoria Parkway
Telephone: (513) 745-3202

UNIVERSITY OF DAYTON
Dayton, Ohio 45469

Dayton is an attractive Ohio industrial city between
Cincinnati and the state capital, Columbus. It is a city
of 28 bridges — where the Great Miami River is joined
by the Stillwater and Mad Rivers and Wolf Creek.
Wright-Patterson Air Force Base is nearby, supplementing
the many important local companies. Besides many
associations with industrial history — the Wright Brothers,
automobile self-starters, the cash register — there are
many cultural and recreational attractions in the area.
The Art Institute and Museum of Natural History,
Carillon Park, and Aulwood Audubon Center, a wildlife
refuge and educational and recreational center,
among others of note.

ACCOMMODATIONS
Single room — $5.50 per person per day
Double room — $4.00 per person per day
Pets are not permitted.
Accommodations are available to students, alumni, adults,
families and prospective matriculants.

MEALS
Cafeteria (typical prices)
Breakfast — $1.10
Lunch — $1.35
Dinner — $1.85

ACTIVITIES (on campus or nearby)
Tennis, basketball and swimming.

AVAILABLE DATES
May 1 — August 1
Advance reservations are required.

CONTACT
Mr. Edwin H. Melhuish
Director of Housing
300 College Park
Telephone: (513) 229-3317

OHIO

HIRAM COLLEGE
Hiram, Ohio 44234

Midway between Cleveland and the Pennsylvania border, Hiram is in Ohio dairy and poultry country. The southern shores of Lake Erie are 30 miles away. Cleveland's cultural benefits are many and near enough to be enjoyed.

ACCOMMODATIONS
Single room—$10.00 per person per day
Double room—$15.00 per day
Baths are shared. Pets are not permitted. Linens and maid service are included.
Accommodations are available to students, alumni, adults, families and prospective matriculants.

MEALS
Cafeteria (typical prices)
Breakfast — $1.50
Lunch — $2.00
Dinner — $2.50
A coffee shop is available.

ACTIVITIES (on campus or nearby)
Swimming, golf and tennis. There is a 25¢ charge for swimming. Sea World of Ohio, Blossom Center, Cleveland Browns' summer camp, and a canoe center.

AVAILABLE DATES
Year round.
Advance reservations are preferred.

CONTACT
Mr. Robert Turner
Director of Student Center and Conferences
Kennedy Center
Telephone: (216) 569-3211, extension 294

KENT STATE UNIVERSITY
Kent, Ohio 44242

Kent is a scenic rural town commonly referred to as the
"tree city." The University is one of the largest in Ohio
with a wide variety of cultural and recreational activities,
including its own golf course. The beautiful 8,456-acre
West Branch State Park, near Kent, offers swimming,
fishing, boating and camping. The cities that surround
Kent each have their own interesting attractions: the
Stan Hewitt Mansion and tours of the Goodyear Tire
Company in Akron; the famous Football Hall of Fame
in Canton; the Hale Homestead in Bath; the Blossom
Music Center, just outside Kent. Stop at the Carousel
Dinner Theatre, in Ravenna, for good food and enter-
tainment. And, don't miss nearby Cuyahog Falls.

ACCOMMODATIONS
Single room — $6.50 per person per day;
$45.50 per person per week
Double room — $5.25 per person per day;
$36.75 per person per week
Accommodations are available at the Korb Guest House.
Pets and illegal drugs are not permitted; no alcoholic
beverages in public areas. Baths are shared. Linens and
maid service are included in the fee.
Accommodations are available to students, alumni, adults,
families, small children, prospective matriculants,
conferences, groups and transients with some
university affiliation.

MEALS
There is a cafeteria, snack bar and restaurant on campus.
Prices vary according to selection.

ACTIVITIES (on campus or nearby)
On campus: lighted tennis courts, handball, basketball,
volleyball, indoor swimming, 18-hole golf course.
Off-campus: movies, fishing, lake swimming, hiking in
nearby park, boating on nearby reservoir. Various types
of athletic equipment are available from the Athletic
Department.

AVAILABLE DATES
Year round.
Reservations are suggested.

CONTACT
Mr. Tim Strawn
Manager, Korb Guest House
Rt. 59
Telephone: (216) 678-3550

RIO GRANDE COLLEGE
Rio Grande, Ohio 45674

Rio Grande is in southern Ohio, near Gallipolis and
Point Pleasant, West Virginia, where the first battle of
the Revolutionary War was fought. The Ohio River offers
wide-ranging recreational attractions, forming the
boundary between Ohio, West Virginia and Kentucky.
The State House Memorial in Gallipolis is a restored
tavern which was an important lodging house for
many prominent visitors.

ACCOMMODATIONS
Double room — $3.50 per person per day
Linens are $1.00 additional.
Accommodations are available to students, alumni, adults,
families and prospective matriculants.

MEALS
A cafeteria and coffee shop are available.

ACTIVITIES (on campus or nearby)
Swimming, boating, fishing and tennis.

AVAILABLE DATES
June 1 — August 22
Advance reservations are required.

CONTACT
Mr. W. O. Smeltzer
Telephone: (614) 245-5353, extension 30

THE COLLEGE OF STEUBENVILLE
Steubenville, Ohio 43952

Steel mills, coal and shipbuilding started Steubenville on the road to becoming a major industrial town. Today, these industries are joined by chemical, ferro-alloy and paper manufacturing. Situated on the Ohio River, Steubenville was named for Baron Frederick von Steuben, a Revolutionary War figure.

ACCOMMODATIONS
Single room — $7.50 per person per day;
$50.00 per person per week
Double room — $5.00 per person per day;
$25.00 per person per week
Baths are shared. Pets are not permitted.
Accommodations are available to students, alumni, adults, families and prospective matriculants.

MEALS
Cafeteria (typical prices)
Breakfast — $1.40
Lunch — $1.70
Dinner — $2.25
A coffee shop is available.

ACTIVITIES (on campus or nearby)
Belleview Park (nominal fees are charged), J. C. Williams Health Center, Three River Stadium, museums, theatre and recreational areas. The Pittsburgh Arts Festival takes place in June and the Oglebay Art Series exhibits during the summer months.

AVAILABLE DATES
June 1 — August 15
Reservations must be made one month in advance for groups only.

CONTACT
Mr. Robert M. Ruday
Director of Conference Services
J. C. Williams College Center
Telephone: (614) 283-3771, extension 235

UNIVERSITY OF TOLEDO
Toledo, Ohio 43606

Toledo began as a settlement around Fort Industry in
1794, where the Maumee River flows into Lake Erie.
The Indians were defeated here at the Battle of Fallen
Timbers and signed over their rights to the land. Its Art
Museum contains one of the great collections of glass
as well as paintings by famous European and American
artists, artifacts relating to the development of writing
and printing, and other permanent exhibits. There is a
marvelous zoo at the Zoological Gardens which also
contains a museum of natural history, an aquarium,
an indoor trout stream, and a band shell and amphitheatre
for summer theatre. The observation deck, at the overseas
cargo center, provides a fascinating view of this large
port's shipping activity. You can ride on antique railroad
cars at the Toledo, Lake Erie and Western Railway on
Secor Road. Harness racing is held at Raceway Park
from early June through July. On campus are a 47-acre
arboretum and Ritter Planetarium.

ACCOMMODATIONS
Fees vary from $4.00 to $10.00 per person per night.
Accommodations are available to the general public.

MEALS
Information is not available.

ACTIVITIES (on campus or nearby)
Off campus: tennis, picnicking, hiking, nature walks,
swimming, fishing at local parks. Boating, yachting and
fishing on Maumee River and Lake Erie.

AVAILABLE DATES
June 30 — September 1
Reservations are required.

CONTACT
Housing Office
Telephone: (419) 537-2941

URBANA COLLEGE
Urbana, Ohio 43078

In central Ohio, where farm products and industry
create a stable economy, Urbana is situated in a fertile
valley between the Mad and Darby Rivers. Approximately
40 miles to the east is the capital city of Columbus; the
metropolis of Cincinnati is a two-hour drive to the south.
Ohio Caverns and Piatt Castle provide the traveler with
a touch of history and natural beauty.

ACCOMMODATIONS
Single room — $8.25 per person per day
Double room — $6.25 per person per day
Suite (3 bedrooms, 1 living room, 2 baths) —
$40.00 per day; accommodates up to 6 people.
Baths are shared. Pets and alcoholic beverages
are not permitted.
Accommodations are available to students, alumni, adults,
families and prospective matriculants.

MEALS
Cafeteria (typical prices)
Breakfast — $1.10
Lunch   — $1.65
Dinner — $2.50

ACTIVITIES (on campus or nearby)
Tennis, basketball, track, swimming and water sports.

AVAILABLE DATES
June 20 — August 30
Advance reservations are required.

CONTACT
Business Manager - Controller
Oak Hall
College Way
Telephone: (513) 652-1301

WILMINGTON COLLEGE
Wilmington, Ohio 45177

On campus, visitors to Wilmington can hear the Simon Goodman Memorial Carillon. In town, tools, implements and kitchenware of pioneer days, and bronzes and paintings by Ohio's Eli Harvey are exhibited at the Clinton County Historical Society Museum. Sample the wines at Tarula Farms Winery. Nearby is Cowan Lake State Park for fishing, boating and swimming, and The Cincinnati Bengals' training camp. For touring, Dayton, Cincinnati and Columbus are about an hour's drive.

ACCOMMODATIONS
Single room — $3.50 per person per day;
$24.50 per person per week
Double room — $2.50 per person per day;
$17.50 per person per week
Linen service is $1.50 additional for the first night.
Maid service is $1.50 per day additional.
Baths are shared. Pets are not permitted.
Accommodations are available to students, alumni, adults, families and prospective matriculants.

MEALS
Cafeteria (typical prices)
Breakfast — $ .99
Lunch — $1.36
Dinner — $1.93

ACTIVITIES (on campus or nearby)
Kings Island is nearby. Swimming and tennis are available at the college gym for a nominal charge. Plays and concerts are available all year long.

AVAILABLE DATES
Facilities are available all year round.
Advance reservations are required during winter and suggested during summer.

CONTACT
Housing Office, Box 1205
Telephone: (513) 382-6661, extension 242

THE COLLEGE OF WOOSTER
Wooster, Ohio 44691

Again the American theme of industry and agriculture is repeated in Wooster's economy. Its outlying areas are important producers of the wheat, corn and potatoes which are the base of our commodity market. Near Cleveland and Lake Erie to the north, Wooster is an important industrial center and reputed to have been the birthplace of the Christmas tree tradition in the United States.

ACCOMMODATIONS
Single room — $5.00 per person per day
Double room — $4.00 per person per day
Baths are shared. Pets and alcoholic beverages are not permitted. Linens are $1.75 per set, and maid service is $1.00 per day.
Accommodations are available to students, alumni, adults, families and prospective matriculants.

MEALS
Cafeteria (typical prices)
Breakfast — $1.30
Lunch — $1.80
Dinner — $2.60
A coffee shop is available.

ACTIVITIES (on campus or nearby)
A nine-hole golf course, 14 hard-surfaced tennis courts, natatoriums (hours arranged for groups), bowling lanes and billiards, public swimming pools (prevailing fees for lifeguard) and Dinner-Theatre In-The-Round. Nearby are Ohio Agricultural Research and Development Center. Wayne County Historical Museum, Canal Fulton Summer Theatre, Blossom Music Center and Kingwood Center.

AVAILABLE DATES
June 22 — August 30
The Wooster Inn, operated by Wooster College, is open all year. Rates upon request.
Reservations are required one week in advance.

CONTACT
Miss Esther Graber, Coordinator of Conferences
Lowry Center
Telephone: (216) 264-1234, extension 318

NORTHWESTERN OKLAHOMA STATE UNIVERSITY
Alva, Oklahoma 73717

Alva, a town of about 8,000, sits in the wheat belt of the country. Wheat and cattle are its major industries. It is located near the Kansas and Texas State lines — Kansas is about 15 miles away and Texas about 80 miles. Near the town is Alabaster Caverns State Park which houses the world's largest gypsum cave (almost 2000 years old); Little Sahara State Park provides sand dune buggy rides, camels to pet and feed, and a lookout tower. Great Plains State Park has playgrounds and areas for swimming, water-skiing, boating and fishing and Boiling Springs State Park is a real oasis on the plains. In Alva be sure to visit Cherokee Strip Museum with its historical artifacts, and the Hatfield Park and Zoo.

ACCOMMODATIONS
Groups of 10 or more — $3.00 per person per day
Groups of less than 10 — $5.00 per person per day
Baths are shared. Linens are provided. Pets are not permitted.
Accommodations are available to students, alumni, adults, families, prospective matriculants, school groups and church groups.

MEALS
Cafeteria (typical prices)
Breakfast — $1.75
Lunch — $2.00
Dinner — $2.00
There is also a snack bar on campus and restaurants located off campus.

ACTIVITIES (on campus or nearby)
Fishing; hiking; horseback riding; dune-buggy riding; golfing; tennis; bowling; spelunking; boating; water-skiing.

AVAILABLE DATES
Year round.
Advance reservations are required.

CONTACT
Mr. Cecil Perkins, Housing Director
Percefull Fieldhouse
Telephone: (405) 327-1700

SOUTHEASTERN STATE COLLEGE
Durant, Oklahoma 74701

In the heart of Oklahoma's Red River Valley, Durant prospered with farms and cattle, and now is a popular resort area. Gracious mansions, beautiful magnolia trees and gardens enhance this fine town on U.S. Route 70 in southern Oklahoma. The route courses across the state, bisecting the oldest Choctaw Indian settlement in Oklahoma. Ten miles west of Durant is Lake Texoma, one of the largest man-made lakes in the world, where fishing, boating, swimming and water-skiing opportunities abound.

ACCOMMODATIONS
Single room — $3.50 per person per day;
$20.00 per person per week
Double room — $3.00 per person per day;
$18.00 per person per week
Suite — $12.00 per person per day;
$65.00 per person per week
Baths are shared in room accommodations and are private in suites. Linens are $1.50 additional and maid service is $1.00 additional.
Accommodations are available to students, alumni, adults, families and prospective matriculants.

MEALS
Cafeteria (typical prices)
Breakfast — $1.25
Lunch — $1.75
Dinner — $1.75
A coffee shop is available.

ACTIVITIES (on campus or nearby)
Horseback riding, water-skiing and golf (two courses nearby). Recreational facilities include basketball, handball, swimming pool and tennis courts. Family picnics and weekend trips available at Lake Texoma. Boating, fishing, water-skiing and golf equipment are available for rent at Lake Texoma.

AVAILABLE DATES
June 1 — August 15
December 20 — January 20
Reservations are required two weeks in advance.

CONTACT
Mr. William J. Morton
Telephone: (405) 924-0121, extensions 2466 and 2467

NORTHEASTERN STATE COLLEGE
Tahlequah, Oklahoma 74464

Our American Indian heritage has significant roots in
Tahlequah. A constitution in their native tongue, the first
Indian newspaper, and the first commercial telephone line
originated here. Eastern Oklahoma abounds with rivers,
lakes and mountains. Three major Indian reservations
are also located to the east.

ACCOMMODATIONS
Single room — $5.00 per person per day
Double room — $4.00 per person per day
Group rates are available upon request.
Baths are shared. Pets and alcoholic beverages
are not permitted.
Accommodations are available to students, alumni, adults,
families and prospective matriculants.

MEALS
Cafeteria (typical prices)
Breakfast — $1.10
Lunch — $1.35
Dinner — $1.35
Sunday Lunch — $1.60
A coffee shop is available.

ACTIVITIES (on campus or nearby)
Golf, swimming, fishing, tennis, hiking and canoeing.

AVAILABLE DATES
Facilities are available all year round.

CONTACT
Mr. Phillip A. Murphy
Director of Housing
Administration Building 111
Telephone: (918) 456-5511,
extension 3111

SOUTHERN OREGON COLLEGE
Ashland, Oregon 97520

Ashaland, situated in the lush Rogue River Valley, draws thousands of tourists every year. Its famous mineral springs produce lithia water which is pumped through the fountains in the city's lovely plaza. The Rogue River National Forest rises on three sides of the city. The park is the site of an Indian war, where you can hike, fish for salmon and steelhead and trout, and picnic. Lithia Park, adjacent to the City Plaza, with woodland, ponds and nature trails, provides tennis, horseshoe pitching, picnicking, zoo, and band concerts.

ACCOMMODATIONS
Single room — $4.00 - $5.00 per person per day
Double room — $6.00 - $7.00 per day
Accommodations are available to community, religious and community groups.

MEALS
Information not available.

ACTIVITIES (on campus or nearby)
Off campus: swimming, fishing, water sports, pack trips in surrounding areas.

AVAILABLE DATES
June 15 — September 15
Reservations are required.

CONTACT
Housing Officer
Siskiyou Boulevard
Telephone: (503) 492-2547

OREGON STATE UNIVERSITY
Corvallis, Oregon 97330

OREGON

Visitors to the college may visit the Memorial Union, which houses the outstanding William Henry Price Collection of paintings and holds continuing exhibits of well-known artists. Also on campus is the interesting Horner Museum with exhibits of minerals, mounted animals and birds, antiques, pioneer memorabilia and Indian artifacts. The nearby Siuslaw National Forest is a beautiful area, including 50 miles of ocean front, beaches, and overlooks. In the Forest is the highest peak in the coastal range, Marys Peak, where you can climb, hike and picnic. Fishing is available at streams, lakes and the ocean and hunting is excellent. About an hour's drive from Corvallis are the sister cities of Springfield and Eugene. While here you can tour the Weyerhaeuser plant which manufactures wood products, and take advantage of all the outdoor recreational facilities in the 10 parks, forests and dams in the area.

ACCOMMODATIONS
Fees vary from $3.00 - $7.00 per person per day. Accommodations are available to the general public.

MEALS
Information is not available

ACTIVITIES (on campus or nearby)
World Championship Timber Carnival in Albany, July 4 weekend. Picnicking, etc. at Avery Park. Eugene: Rhododendron Festival, 2nd week in May; Emerald Empire Roundup, mid-July; Lane County Fair, late August. Swimming, hiking, mountain climbing, fishing, boating, water sports, etc. at nearby parks and forests.

AVAILABLE DATES
Year round
Reservations are required.

CONTACT
Housing Officer
Monroe and Washington Streets
Telephone: (503) 754-1771

MARYLHURST COLLEGE
Marylhurst, Oregon 97036

Marylhurst is located in the beautiful area of Lake
Oswego, just 14 miles south of Portland. Portland, in the
gorgeous Willamette Valley, has everything a visitor
could desire: skiing, hunting, fishing, mountain climbing,
and a handsome cosmopolitan metropolitan area.
While here see the only breeding herd of elephants
in America, at the zoo which also contains Antarctic
penguins, a good collection of other animals, and a
children's theatre and zoo. The Bybee-Howell House, on
Sauvie Island, is a pioneer home with period furnishings.
Pittock Mansion, in Pittock Acres Park, is beautifully
situated and contains some good antiques. The Oregon
Museum of Science and Industry contains a planetarium,
and excellent exhibits of science and nature. Portland's
Art Museum holds the Gebauer collection of West African
art as well as a notable collection of New and Old World
and Oriental arts. For shopping, visit the Lloyd Shopping
Center, one of the nation's largest downtown shopping areas.

ACCOMMODATIONS
Fees range from $5.00 - $8.00 per person per day.
Visitors must stay a minimum of 2 days.

MEALS
Information is not available.

ACTIVITIES (on campus or nearby)
Swimming, fishing, picnicking, boating, hiking and sight-
seeing at parks in the Portland area; golf in Portland;
industrial tours of Jantzen, Inc. and Pendleton Woolen
Mills. Pacific International Live Stock Show in
Portland (October).

AVAILABLE DATES
Year round
Reservations are required.

CONTACT
Housing Officer
Highway #43
Telephone: (503) 636-8141

UNIVERSITY OF PORTLAND
Portland, Oregon 97203

More than half of Oregon's people live in and around
Portland and other towns of the Willamette Valley, a
fertile, rain-blessed trough between the Cascade Range
and the lower mountains, facing the state's spectacular
400-mile coast. The recreations of beach and mountain
are easily accessible. Portland, Oregon's largest city,
is on both banks of the north-flowing Willamette River,
just south of its confluence with the Columbia. Its busy
fresh-water harbor, ample hydroelectric power for
smokeless, smogless energy, and picturesque land and
sea scapes enhance its attractiveness to visitors.

ACCOMMODATIONS
Single room — $5.00 per person per day;
$35.00 per person per week
Double room — $7.00 per person per day;
$49.00 per person per week
Suite — $7.00 per person per day;
$49.00 per person per week
Apartment — $10.00 per day; $70.00 per week
Trailer Site — $3.00 per day; $21.00 per week
Baths are shared and private. Pets are not permitted.
Accommodations are available to students, alumni, adults,
families and prospective matriculants.

MEALS
Cafeteria (typical prices)
Breakfast — $1.05
Lunch — $1.35
Dinner — $1.95
A coffee shop is available.

ACTIVITIES (on campus or nearby)
Weight room, pool tables, track, playing courts and fields.
Information is available for other activity programs.
Audio-visual and athletic equipment available for rental.

AVAILABLE DATES
Facilities are available year round.

CONTACT
Jan Tirrill
Villa Continuing Education Center
5000 North Willamette Boulevard
Telephone: (503) 283-7269

CEDAR CREST COLLEGE
Allentown, Pennsylvania 18104

Allentown's Pennsylvania Dutch heritage and association with the American Revolution add to the charm and naturalness of its attractive environs. One of the major cities of Lehigh Valley, Allentown is known for the manufacture of machinery, textile, metal products and electrical and electronic equipment. The Delaware River to the east flows through the Pocono Mountains at the Water Gap. Picturesque villages and rolling hills border the river on both the Pennsylvania and New Jersey shores.

ACCOMMODATIONS
Single room — $6.00 per person per day;
$38.50 per person per week
Double room — $6.00 per person per day;
$38.50 per person per week
Baths are shared. Linens are included. Pets and alcoholic beverages are not permitted.
Accommodations are available to students, alumni, adults, families and prospective matriculants.

MEALS
A cafeteria is available.

ACTIVITIES (on campus or nearby)
Tennis, swimming and golf. There are modest fees for both swimming and golf. Attractions include the Art Museum, Liberty Bell replica, and the nearby Pocono Mountains, trout nursery, and county game preserve.

AVAILABLE DATES
June 10 — August 15
Advance reservations are required.

CONTACT
Mr. Richard K. Begbie
Director of College Center
Telephone: (215) 437-4471,
extension 201

LEBANON VALLEY COLLEGE
Annville, Pennsylvania 17003

In the delightful Lebanon Valley, Annville is just five miles from the colorful German-American city of Lebanon. Following the Battle of Trenton many Hessian soldiers were confined here. There's an interesting farmers' market on North 9th Street, open on Friday and Saturday. Fort Zeller, 11 miles east, is one of the state's oldest forts still in existence. It was rebuilt in 1745 and contains a 12-foot wide Queen Anne fireplace in the kitchen. Another "Pennsylvania Dutch" town, Reading, is about 30 miles east. During the Revolution, Reading too served as a prison for captured Hessian and English soldiers. While in Reading, don't miss the Daniel Boone homestead where Boone lived for 16 years before his family moved to North Carolina. Set on 600 acres, there are 18 buildings on this plantation which also contains picnic areas and nature trails. Reading's Pagoda is another "must see" spot: It's a Japanese building anchored to a mountain by thousands of bolts. About 10 miles further east is West Chester, situated in the storm center of the state's Revolutionary War battles: Valley Forge, Brandywine and Paoli.

ACCOMMODATIONS
Single room — $5.00 - $10.00 per person per day
Double room — $10.00 - $15.00 per day
Accommodations are available to the general public.

MEALS
Information is not available.

ACTIVITIES (on campus or nearby)
Industrial tour: Weaver's Lebanon Balogna factory.
Golf: local courses; fee charge. Swimming at Coleman Memorial Park.

AVAILABLE DATES
June 1 — August 25
Reservations are required.

CONTACT
Housing Office
Telephone: (717) 867-3561

HARCUM JUNIOR COLLEGE
Bryn Mawr, Pennsylvania 19010

Bryn Mawr is on the outskirts of Philadelphia, the
Cradle of the Nation, where the Declaration of Independence and the Constitution were drafted and adopted.
Philadelphia was the first capital of the nation and
here Washington served as President and Betsy Ross
sewed the first American flag. The Walking Tour of old
Philadelphia is a pleasant and interesting way to relive
this vital part of American history. Franklin Institute,
near Independence Park, is justly famous for its Science
Museum and Planetarium. There are dozens of old
restored mansions and houses of famous people in
Philadelphia: the Edgar Allen Poe House, and Stanton
Mansion are notable examples. There are submarines,
battleships and other naval vessels at the Naval Shipyard.
The nearby USS *Olympia*, Commodore Dewey's flagship,
is particularly interesting. Two-hour tours of the harbor
on the *Showboat* are available during the summer.
A delightful open air market, open on weekends in the
Society Hill area, features puppets, concerts, and
craft demonstrations.

ACCOMMODATIONS
Single room — $10.00 per person per day
Double room — $20.00 per day
Accommodations are available to the general public.

MEALS
Information is not available.

ACTIVITIES (on campus or nearby)
Philadelphia: Elfreth's Alley Open House Day, 1st
Saturday in June. Freedom Week and Festival of
Fountains, late June - July 4; walking and bus tours;
harbor tours.

AVAILABLE DATES
May 20 — September 1
Reservations are required.

CONTACT
Housing Office
Montgomery and Morris Avenue
Telephone: (215) LA 5-4100

CALIFORNIA STATE COLLEGE
California, Pennsylvania 15419

The town of Washington is about ½ hour's drive from
California. There's a fascinating collection of 32 buildings
here, dating from the late 1700's to 1900. Especially
interesting are the blacksmith shop, wagon shed, general
store and smokehouse. The restored frontier home of
David Bradford, a leader of the "Whiskey Rebellion,"
is also in Washington. Less than an hour away is the
handsome — and clean — industrial giant, Pittsburgh.
Two hill-climbing trolleys — the Monongahela and
Duquesne inclined planes — provide an interesting ride
to observation decks where you can view the city and
its environs. Point State Park contains the Museum
and Block House of Fort Pitt. The city is filled with
modern architectural showpieces, particularly at Gateway
Center which also contains lovely gardens, walks and
fountains. There are so many attractions and events in
Pittsburgh that a visitor should plan several trips.

ACCOMMODATIONS
Single room — $5.00 per person per day
Accommodations are available to the general public.

MEALS
Information is not available.

ACTIVITIES (on campus or nearby)
Sightseeing, hiking. Three Rivers Arts Festival
(Pittsburgh) : Late May - early June.

AVAILABLE DATES
June 1 — August 15
Reservations are required.

CONTACT
Housing Office
Telephone: (412) 938-2281

EAST STROUDSBURG COLLEGE
East Stroudsburg, Pennsylvania

East Stroudsburg is in the Pocono Mountains, famous as a resort area. This is a beautiful section of the state, excellent for short or full-day car tours. Don't miss: Pocono Wild Animal Farm, where some of the animals roam free; Delaware Water Gap, the beautiful gorge where the Delaware River flows through the Kittatinny Mountains; Quiet Valley Farm Museum, with original and reconstructed buildings and a three-room log cabin, where you can see demonstrations of farming; Buck Hill Falls; Bushkill Falls, a truly lovely area of 100-foot waterfalls and a gorge, with native animals and picnicking areas; Winona Five Falls, containing five separate waterfalls in a wooded picnic site. You can hike along the beautiful Appalachian Trail nearby. Lake Wallenpaupack is about twenty miles north of E. Stroudsburg.

ACCOMMODATIONS
Single room — $9.00 per person per day
Double room — $8.00 per person per day
Baths are shared. Children will not be accommodated.
Accommodations are available to married couples, adults.

MEALS
Cafeteria (typical prices)
Breakfast — $1.25
Lunch — $1.75
Dinner — $2.25

ACTIVITIES (on campus or nearby)
Swimming pool, tennis, recreational program, cookouts.
Off-campus: touring, hiking, swimming.

AVAILABLE DATES
June 20 — August 20

CONTACT
Dr. Richard Luce
Telephone: (717) 424-3455

ELIZABETHTOWN COLLEGE
Elizabethtown, Pennsylvania 17022

Midway between Harrisburg and Lancaster, Elizabethtown is located in the fascinating Pennsylvania Dutch
countryside. Nearby are well-tended Pennsylvania Dutch
and Amish farms, and restaurants featuring their unique
cuisine. There are three state parks in the area, numerous
summer theatres, golf courses, and sailing on the Susque-
hanna River. For touring, the Gettysburg Battlefield,
Pennsylvania State Museum, and Hershey Farm are
popular attractions. Other sights to see are Hershey
Flower Gardens, Landis Valley Farm Museum and
Ephrata Cloisters.

ACCOMMODATIONS
Double room — $6.50 per person for first day;
$4.00 per person per day thereafter.
Pets and alcoholic beverages are not permitted.
Accommodations are available to students, alumni, adults,
families and prospective matriculants.

MEALS
Cafeteria (typical prices)
Breakfast — $1.25
Lunch — $1.70
Dinner — $2.25
A coffee shop is available.

ACTIVITIES (on campus or nearby)
Tennis, swimming, ping pong, pool, and bowling (for a
nominal fee). Pennsylvania Dutch Week takes place
from June 29 to July 6 in Kutztown, Pennsylvania.

AVAILABLE DATES
May 13 — May 30
June 9 — July 11
July 14 — August 16
Advance reservations are required.

CONTACT
Mr. Gordon R. Bateman
Student Center
Telephone: (717) 367-1151, extension 210

THIEL COLLEGE
Greenville, Pennsylvania 16125

Greenville is a small, quiet town located approximately
two hours from Cleveland, Ohio and Pittsburgh, Pa.
Pymatuning State Park, near Greenville, offers a large
lake for boating, fishing, picnicking, swimming, hunting,
ice boating and skating in winter. Pittsburgh offers much
in the way of cultural and historic attractions, and a
lively night life. Ride the trollways to Monongahela
Inclined Plane for a lovely sweeping view of the city;
visit the Carnagie Institute; Schenley Park offers tennis,
picnic facilities, swimming, golf, a nature museum, and
Phipps Conservatory. Bring the children to Kennywood
park, one of the largest amusement parks in the country.
Don't miss taking a scenic and relaxing boat ride on the
three rivers (contact: Gateway Clipper, Inc. Monongahela
Wharf, Pittsburgh, Pa.)

ACCOMMODATIONS
Single room—$7.50 per person per day
Double room—$5.00 per person per day
Baths are private in the single rooms, otherwise they
are shared. Linens are provided. Cots can be provided
for a fee of $1.00 per night.
Accommodations are available to students, alumni, adults,
families, prospective matriculants, and conference groups.

MEALS
Cafeteria (typical prices)
Breakfast — $1.25
Lunch — $1.75
Dinner — $2.75
There is a snack bar on campus, and restaurants
located off campus.

ACTIVITIES (on campus or nearby)
On campus: swimming and tennis, both at no charge.
Off campus: hiking, golf, fishing and boating available
at several facilities in the immediate area. Boats available
for rent at nearby lakes.

AVAILABLE DATES
September 1—June 1 (capacity up to 100)
June 1—August 25 (capacity up to 1,200).
Advance reservations are required.

CONTACT
Dr. Jon D. Holstlne
Director of Special Programs
Telephone: (412) 588-7700

JUNIATA COLLEGE
Huntington, Pennsylvania 16652

In the lovely Juniata Valley, Huntingdon is on the site of an old Oneida Indian village. There are two caverns nearby that shouldn't be missed. Lincoln Caverns, 3 miles west, includes the spectacular Diamond Cascade and Frozen Niagara. Beautiful Indian Caverns, 15 miles west, is illuminated and contains relics of Indian history and culture. Look for the Stone Tablet with picture writing. The Swigart Museum, just outside Huntingdon, houses exhibits of early American cars — electric, steam and gas. Altoona is about a half hour's drive from Huntingdon. While here, don't miss the Horseshoe Curve, an incredible achievement of railroad engineering. The curve, with a central angle of 220°, is 2,375 feet long around a grade of 91 feet per mile. Six counties can be viewed from the lookout atop Wopsonock Mountain, near Altoona, while picnicking, swimming, fishing and boating are available at Prince Gallitzin State Park. Don't miss the Animal Safari and Game Preserve in Altoona, where animals roam free.

ACCOMMODATIONS
Single room — $5.00 - $9.00 per person per day
Accommodations are available to the general public.

MEALS
Information is not available.

ACTIVITIES (on campus or nearby)
Lncoln and Indian Caverns; picnicking, fishing, swimming, etc. at Altoona; Blair County Arts Festival (Altoona), mid-July.

AVAILABLE DATES
June 1 — August 15
Reservations are required.

CONTACT
Housing Office
1800 Moore Street
Telephone: (814) 643-4310

DREXEL UNIVERSITY
Philadelphia, Pennsylvania 19104

Philadelphia is a wonderful town for visitors. It has
reclaimed and restored the buildings and sites which were
so intimately tied to the birth of the United States.
The Walking Tour leads the visitor, by pleasant stages,
through such historical treasures as Independence Hall,
with the Liberty Bell, Congress Hall, Old City Hall where
the first Supreme Court sat, Christ Church where some
of the signers are buried, Betsy Ross House, and many
more. There are hundreds of other attractions ranging
from the U.S. Mint, science institutes, and lovely old
mansions to the *Gazela Primeira* in the refurbished
and exciting port area. There are evening concerts at the
open-air Robin Hood Dell, musical and ballet performances
at Temple University, "sound and light" shows and free
entertainment at four different spots in the city,
professional sports and racing, and theatrical performances
in-the-round in West Fairmount Park. It takes several
days to take in all that this city has to offer.

ACCOMMODATIONS
Single room — $5.00 - $11.00 per person per day
Accommodations are available to students.

MEALS
Information is not available.

ACTIVITIES (on campus or nearby)
Festival of Fountains and Freedom Week: late June-July
4 Head House Open Air Market: June-August, Saturdays
and Sundays. See description for other activities.

AVAILABLE DATES
June 25 — September 10

CONTACT
Housing Office
203 North 34th Street
Telephone: (215) 895-2775

UNIVERSITY OF PENNSYLVANIA
Philadelphia, Pennsylvania 19174

Philadelphia is a city of wide-ranging cultural, recreational and historical attractions. Its identity as the birthplace of the nation is enshrined in Independence Hall and the Liberty Bell. A strong civic movement has revitalized the neighborhood, restoring and preserving historic colonial homes in a downtown section called Society Hill. Philadelphia's world-famous orchestra and art museum, its modern shops, the new, glass-fronted skyscrapers of Penn Center and the grassy stretch of the Parkway terminating at its beautiful City Hall are but samples of countless attractions. Ample public transportation makes it easy to get around and see the sights. There's no end of things to see and do.

ACCOMMODATIONS
Single room — $15.00 - $18.00 per person per day;
$90 - $108 per person per week
Double room — $12.00 per person per day;
$72.00 per person per week
Pets are not permitted.
Accommodations are available to students, alumni, and prospective matriculants.

MEALS
A cafeteria is available.

ACTIVITIES (on campus or nearby)
Access to all University facilities for a nominal fee. There is a $1.00 advance reservation fee for squash and tennis courts.

AVAILABLE DATES
June 1 — August 15
Advance reservations are required.

CONTACT
Mr. Paul R. Rubincam, Jr.
1925 House, Building BD
3940 Locust Walk
Telephone: (215) 594-6843

CARLOW COLLEGE
Pittsburgh, Pennsylvania 15213

The steel industry has made Pittsburgh a world leader in the manufacture and distribution of steel. The "Iron Masters" and other industrial, commercial and financial leaders built the modern glass skyscrapers and created the green parks for which Pittsburgh is now known. Theatre and the arts are represented by the famed Pittsburgh Symphony Orchestra, the Carnegie Museum and Art Gallery, and other institutions. The Allegheny River, joining the Ohio, forms America's largest inland river port, which handles more than 50 million tons of shipping a year. Because of Pittsburgh's early importance in the coal and steel industries, it became the birthplace in 1881 of the American Federation of Labor.

ACCOMMODATIONS
Single room — $5.00 - $8.00 per person per day
Double room — $5.00 - $10.00 per day
Children will not be accommodated.
Maximum stay: 7 days.
Accommodations are available to adults.

MEALS
Information is not available.

ACTIVITIES (on campus or nearby)
Pittsburgh has baseball, hockey and football teams, thus sporting events are plentiful. Fort Duquesne is nearby, as is the Three Rivers Stadium and the Buhl Planetary.

AVAILABLE DATES
Year round.
Reservations are required.

CONTACT
Housing Office
3333 Fifth Avenue
Telephone: (412) 683-5827

CARNEGIE INSTITUTE
Pittsburgh, Pennsylvania 15213

Pittsburgh has been transformed from an epically dirty, smog-covered city into a handsome, modern, clean city with soaring new skyscrapers constructed of aluminum, glass and steel. It has 22 parks, many recreation centers and pools, an an active river port. Gateway Center is a haven for the foot-weary: skyscrapers surround a two-acre garden lushly planted with flowering shrubs and seasonal flowers bordering lovely walks. Highland Park Zoos contain a zoo with 1,500 animals, a children's zoo and an underground zoo for nocturnal burrowing animals. The zoo also has facilities for tennis, swimming and picnicking. Buhl Planetarium has daily sky shows and the night sky can be viewed through the telescope at Allegheny Observatory (by appointment) from April through October. Three boats provide interesting day and night cruises on the three rivers of this inland port.

ACCOMMODATIONS
Single room — $3.00 - $5.00 per person per night
Maximum stay: two days.
Accommodations are available to single adults (no families or married couples).

MEALS
Information is not available.

ACTIVITIES (on campus or nearby)
On campus: Carnegie Museum of Natural History and the Museum of Art; no charge. Professional sports at Three Rivers Stadium. Three Rivers Arts Festival: Gateway Center, late May - early June.

AVAILABLE DATES
April 15 — August 20

CONTACT
Housing Office
1065 Morewood Avenue
Telephone: (412) 582-9580

POINT PARK COLLEGE
Pittsburgh, Pennsylvania 15222

The steel industry has made Pittsburgh a world leader in the manufacture and distribution of steel. The "Iron Masters" and other industrial, commercial and financial leaders built the modern glass skyscrapers and created the green parks for which Pittsburgh is now known. Theatre and the arts are represented by the famed Pittsburgh Symphony Orchestra, the Carnegie Museum and Art Gallery, and other institutions. The Allegheny River, joining the Ohio, forms America's largest inland river port, which handles more than 50 million tons of shipping a year. Because of Pittsburgh's early importance in the coal and steel industries, it became the birthplace in 1881 of the American Federation of Labor.

ACCOMMODATIONS
Double room — $10.00 per person per day
(includes three meals)
The rooms are located in what was once one of Pittsburgh's finest hotels. Baths are private. Linens are included. Pets and children under 12 years of age are not permitted.
Accommodations are available to students, alumni, adults, families and prospective matriculants.

MEALS
A cafeteria and coffee shop are available.

ACTIVITIES (on campus or nearby)
Numerous historical, scenic and recreational sites are available. The Allegheny Mountains are nearby.

AVAILABLE DATES
May 20 — August 31 (unlimited vacancies)
September 1 — May 20 (limited vacancies)
Reservations are required at least one week in advance.

CONTACT
Mr. Francis J. Gruden, III
Director of Residence Halls
201 Wood Street
Telephone: (412) 391-4111

CABRINI COLLEGE
Radnor, Pennsylvania 19087

Cabrini College is a small quiet school with Valley Forge Park and Norristown nearby. During the bitter, dark winter of 1777-78, 11,000 soldiers were encamped in Valley Forge. 3,000 of these men died from extreme cold, starvation, and illness. Valley Forge has since become a memorial park in their honor. During the spring, pink and white dogwood blossoms burst into delicate color, and can be seen in full view from the 75 ft. observation tower. The park also has: tours, restoration sights of the hospital and the barracks, a chapel, and many other memorial tributes to those soldiers. Norristown is a neighboring city where the Dutch, German, Swedish, Welsh, and English immigrants all left their mark. The city houses many industries and is a retail center. The Mill Grove (Audubon Wildlife Sanctuary) built in 1762 should not be missed.

ACCOMMODATIONS
Single room — $10.00 per person per day
Double room — $7.50 per person per day
Some rooms can accommodate 3 or 4 people, group rates are given on request. Baths are shared. Linen service is provided for a fee. Pets and children under 12 years are not permitted.
Accommodations are available to general public.

MEALS
Cafeteria (typical prices)
Breakfast — $1.00
Lunch — $1.50
Dinner — $2.25

ACTIVITIES (on campus or nearby)
Tennis, swimming, fishing, hiking, horseback riding, and golf.

AVAILABLE DATES
May 20 — August 20

CONTACT
V.P. for Business and Finance
Eage Rd. and King of Prussia Rd.
Telephone: (215) 687-2100

LINCOLN UNIVERSITY
U.S. Route #1, Pennsylvania 19352

Lincoln University, founded in 1854, is the first college begun for predominately black students. Philadelphia and Baltimore, Md. are within easy reach of the college. Once in Philadelphia the visitor will find a vast variety of historic sights to see. The Walking Tour of Old Philadelphia consists of 29 historic buildings that bring you back to 1776. The Edgar Allen Poe House, where Poe wrote *The Raven, The Gold Bug* and many other classics, is a popular stop in "Philly." Take another day to see Baltimore, Md. with its wide selection of museums, monuments, parks, zoos, and tours to suite the most discriminating tourist. Some interesting stops to make are: The Lexington Market, a famous indoor market with over a 100 merchants inside; The Lloyd Street Synagogue, the oldest Synagogue in Maryland housing a museum of Jewish ceremonial objects; and the Star Spangled Banner Flag Museum and the 1812 War Museum.

ACCOMMODATIONS
Single room — $10.00 per person
Double room — $5.00 per person
Baths are shared. Pets are not permitted.
Accommodations are available to general public.

MEALS
Restaurants are located off campus.

ACTIVITIES (on campus or nearby)
Tennis, swimming, arcade games, pool, ping pong, gymnasium.

AVAILABLE DATES
May 12 — August 8
Reservations are required.

CONTACT
Housing Director
Telephone: (215) 932-8300

NORTHEASTERN CHRISTIAN JUNIOR COLLEGE
Villanova, Pennsylvania 19085

Villanova is a gracious, tree-lined town including many stately mansions in the prestigious "Main Line" area— a string of suburban communities north and west of Philadelphia on the Schuylkill River and Lancaster Pike. Many colleges and universities dot the area, named for the commuter train service on the Penn-Central Railroad. Adjoining Villanova are the Valley Forge State Park, and a year-round theatre, the Valley Forge Music Fair. All of Philadelphia's wide-ranging cultural, recreational and historical attractions are conveniently accessible. Independence Hall and the the Liberty Bell. The restored historic homes of Society Hill. The renowned Philadelphia Orchestra, numerous art museums, Franklin Institute, Free Public Library, Science City—to name but a few. No end of things to see and do.

ACCOMMODATIONS
Double room—$4.00 per person per day; $28.00 per person per week
Baths are private in each suite of rooms. Linens are $2.00 additional. Pets and alcoholic beverages are not permitted. Smoking is restricted.
Accommodations are available to students, alumni, adults, families and prospective matriculants.

MEALS
Cafeteria (typical prices)
Breakfast — $1.25
Lunch — $1.50
Dinner — $2.25
A coffee shop is available.

ACTIVITIES (nearby)
Fishing, hiking, boating, tennis, bowling, ice skating. Special tours and activities planned for the summer of 1976 Bicentennial. Write for free brochure.

AVAILABLE DATES
May 6—August 30
Advance reservations are required.

CONTACT
Mrs. Sara Bills or Mrs. Valerie Jacoby
Public Information Office
1860 Montgomery Avenue
Telephone: (215) LA5-6780, extension 22

KINGS COLLEGE
Wilkes-Barre, Pennsylvania 18711

Wilkes-Barre, named for two English Members of
Parliament who championed the cause of the American
Colonies, has had a checkered history. The Pennamite-
Yankee War was fought by Pennsylvania and Connecticut
over possession of the area from 1771 until 1800 when
Connecticut gave up her claim. The city was burned
twice: during the Revolution and again in 1782 by
Connecticut settlers. The city was once the anthracite-
producing center of the world but now has a diversity
of industries. The Swetland Homestead demonstrates
family life and architectural styles from 1797 to 1864.
Forty Fort, 2 miles north, contains the site of the first
settlement of the Wyoming Valley and the 1807 Forty
Fort Meetinghouse. A monument in the city marks the
site where settlers were massacred by Iroquois Indians
in 1778 after the British captured Forty Fort.

ACCOMMODATIONS
Single room — $5.00 per person per night
Accommodations are available to the general public.

MEALS
Information is not available.

ACTIVITIES (on campus or nearby)
Off campus: swimming, fishing, boating, amusement area
at Harvey's Lake. Industrial tours: contact Luzeme
County Promotion Agency, 301 Market Street.

AVAILABLE DATES
June 1 — August 15
Reservations are required.

CONTACT
Housing Office
East Hall
North Main Street
Telephone: (717) 824-9931

ROGER WILLIAMS COLLEGE
Bristol, Rhode Island 02809

America's Cup, the hallowed 12-meter yacht race in which every helmsman dreams of showing his boatmanship, and Bristol have an important attachment. A local boatyard has built many of the Cup's winners. For boating and fishing, the Bristol peninsula is hard to surpass. Surf pounds on the rocky shores, where all manner of marine life prevails. Buzzards Bay and Nantucket Sound are within sailing distance to the east and Block Island Sound to the west. Bristol port was important in the early nineteenth century hey-day of the New England clipper ships.

ACCOMMODATIONS
Single room—$5.00 per person per day
Double room—$4.00 per person per day
Baths are shared. Pets and drugs are not permitted. Accommodations are available to students, alumni, adults, families and prospective matriculants.

MEALS
Cafeteria (typical prices)
Breakfast — $1.50
Lunch — $1.50
Dinner — $2.75
A snack bar is available.

ACTIVITIES (on campus or nearby)
Swimming, tennis and golf.

AVAILABLE DATES
July 1—August 31
Advance reservations are required.

CONTACT
Housing Director
Ferry Road
Telephone (401) 255-2106

UNIVERSITY OF RHODE ISLAND
Kingston, Rhode Island 02881

Kingston is a village noted for fine specimens of
colonial architecture in a state measuring 37 by 48
miles. This scenic Liliput wedged between Massachusetts
and Connecticut nevertheless has a 400-mile coastline
and a diversity of activity equalled by few domains.
Bristol, Providence, Narragansett, Block Island and
Newport, all have stories to tell and paths to explore.

ACCOMMODATIONS
Single room — $9.00 per person per day;
$63.00 per person per week
Double room — $7.00 per person per day;
$49.00 per person per week
Baths are shared. Linens and maid service included.
Pets are not permitted.
Accommodations are available to general public.

MEALS
A cafeteria and coffee shop are available.

ACTIVITIES (on campus or nearby)
Swimming, fishing, tennis and hiking. Picnics and
scenic tours are available. There is a 50¢ charge for
use of the swimming pool.

AVAILABLE DATES
June — August
Advance reservations are required.

CONTACT
Summer Housing Office,
Manager of Dormitory Services
Telephone: (401) 792-2215

NORTHERN STATE COLLEGE
Aberdeen, South Dakota 57401

The author of *The Wizard of Oz*, L. Frank Baum, was
born in Aberdeen, as were the Fischer quintuplets.
The Wylie Zoo has an interesting collection of South
Dakota animals, including eagles, deer, coyote and buffalo.
There are exhibits of pioneer and Indian life in the
Dacotah Prairie Museum, as well as period rooms and
an art gallery. Swimming, picnicking and fishing facilities
are provided at Mina and Richmond Lake, both near
Aberdeen. The town of Redfield, about 40 miles south,
is near Fisher Grove State Park with historical landmarks
and facilities for outdoor sports. West of Aberdeen,
within an hour's drive, is Fort Sisseton, built in 1864
as a protection for settlers against local Indian forces.
The famous scout, Samuel J. Brown, left here during a
blizzard to warn traders at Ruilliard's Trading Post
that Sioux were going to raid the area. At the post he
discovered that a peace treaty had been signed with the
Sioux, so he returned through the blizzard to the Fort,
55 miles away, to prevent the Army from marching
against the Sioux. He was in time but, because of the
extreme cold and long ride he had endured, he was
paralyzed for life.

ACCOMMODATIONS
Single room — $4.00 - $5.00 per person per day
Accommodations are available to the general public.

MEALS
Information is not available.

ACTIVITIES (on campus or nearby)
Off campus: swimming, picnicking and fishing at nearby
recreation areas.

AVAILABLE DATES
May 15 — August 15

CONTACT
Housing Office
Telephone: (605) 622-2566

UNIVERSITY OF SOUTH DAKOTA
Springfield, South Dakota 57062

Springfield is located in the lowlands on the Lewis and
Clark Lake, part of the historic Missouri River, which is
North Dakota's and Nebraska's border. Farmland, cattle
and horses enhance the rural charm of the town, which is
an agricultural center of South Dakota.

ACCOMMODATIONS
Single room — $1.00 per person per day;
$5.00 per person for five days
Double room — $1.00 per person per day;
$5.00 per person for five days
Baths are shared. There is no additional charge for
linens. Pets and alcoholic beverages are not permitted.
Accommodations are available to students and
prospective matriculants.

MEALS
Cafeteria (typical prices)
Breakfast — $1.00
Lunch — $1.50
Dinner — $2.00

ACTIVITIES (on campus or nearby)
Swimming, fishing, tennis, hiking and golf. Gavins Point
and Fort Randall Dams are nearby.

AVAILABLE DATES
June 3 — August 9
Advance reservations are not required.

CONTACT
Mr. David Lorenz
Student Union
Telephone: (605) 369-2287;
if no answer call, (605) 369-2293.

KNOXVILLE COLLEGE
Knoxville, Tennessee 37921

Knoxville began as a trading post on the Wilderness Road, and was settled by veterans of the Revolutionary War. During the Civil War the city was occupied by Confederate and Federal troops. The Seige of Knoxville which caused heavy damage to the city, resulted in the permanent occupation by the Northern forces. There are several ante bellum mansions in the city that are well worth a visit. Confederate Memorial Hall was the headquarters of Gen. James Longstreet during the Siege. On a wall of its tower are three drawings labeled "men who were shot up here." James White's Fort contains seven block houses, each holding historical artifacts and furniture of the settlement period. Governor Blount Home, the first frame house built west of the Alleghenics (1792) and the Craighead Jackson House across the street have furnishings of the period. There are two superb auto tours no visitor to Knoxville should miss: the Newfound Gap Highway and the Scenic Loop, a magnificent 100-mile trip to the Great Smoky Mountains National Park.

ACCOMMODATIONS
Single room — $6.00 - $12.00 per person per day
Double room — $3.00 - $6.00 per person per day
Accommodations are available to the general public.

MEALS
Information is not available.

ACTIVITIES (on campus or nearby)
Off campus: theatre productions in-the-round, Carousel Theatre. Dogwood Arts Festival: 10 days in April. Tours of Tennessee University Arboretum.

AVAILABLE DATES
Year round.

CONTACT
Housing Office
901 College Street
Telephone: (615) 546-0751

COVENANT COLLEGE
Lookout Mountain, Tennessee 37350

The 2,100-foot elevation of Lookout Mountain, where the College is situated, offers a spectacular view which draws millions of visitors. On a clear day you can see seven different states from Top-of-the-Mountain-View. Within walking distance are trenches occupied by Confederate soldiers over a century ago. A few miles away is the Chickamauga National Battlefield. On Lookout Mountain are: Confederama, an electronic display of the Civil War in miniature as it related to Chattanooga and Lookout Mountain; a steep, exciting cable car ride on the edge of the mountain, on the Incline Railway; Rock City Gardens, a lovely walk-through geological and botanical display, which includes Fairyland Caverns and Mother Goose Village.

ACCOMMODATIONS
Single room—$12.00 per person per day;
$72.00 per person per week
Double room—$10.00 per person per day;
$60.00 per person per week
All rates include room and board. Children under 5 are free. Other rates upon request. Baths are shared or private, depending upon accommodations. Linens: $2.00. Maid service: $5.00 per room. Pets, smoking, drinking are not permitted.
Accommodations are available to the general public and conference groups.

MEALS
Cafeteria (typical prices)
Breakfast — $1.50
Lunch — $2.00
Dinner — $2.50
A cafeteria and snack bar are on campus; restaurants are off campus.

ACTIVITIES (on campus or nearby)
On campus: tennis, volleyball, basketball, 2 athletic fields, hiking and swimming; no fee. Off campus: see description of area above.

AVAILABLE DATES
Christmas: December 20—January 10
Summer: May 15—August 15
Reservations are suggested.

CONTACT
Jay A. Lykins, Conference Director
Telephone: (404) 831-6531

BETHEL COLLEGE
McKenzie, Tennessee 38201

McKenzie is located in the beautiful, rolling hill country of northeast Tennessee, only 40 miles from two of the world's largest man-made lakes — Kentucky and Barkley. Between these huge lakes, on a 170,000 acre wooded isthmus, the Tennessee Valley Authority has developed the land between the Lakes, a National Recreation and Conservation Education area. Here camping, fishing, sailing, speed boating and hiking are ideal.

ACCOMMODATIONS
Single room — $5.00 per person per day;
$30.00 per person per week
Double room — $5.00 per person per day;
$30.00 per person per week
Suite — $15.00 per day; $75.00 per week
Trailer site — $3.00 per day; $15.00 per week.
Baths are shared and private. Pets and alcoholic beverages are not permitted.
Accommodations are available to students, alumni, adults, families and prospective matriculants.

MEALS
Cafeteria (typical prices)
Breakfast — $1.00
Lunch — $1.25
Dinner — $1.40

ACTIVITIES (on campus or nearby)
Tennis, swimming, fishing and boating. Family picnic areas are plentiful.

AVAILABLE DATES
June 15 — August 15
Advance reservations are requested.

CONTACT
Mr. William L. Cottrell, Jr.
President
Telephone: (901) 352-5321 or (901) 352-5322

TENNESSEE STATE UNIVERSITY
Nashville, Tennessee 37203

Nashville was founded by James Robertson on Christmas Day, 1779. It was the scene of an important Civil War battle in 1864 when General Hood failed in an attempt to retake the city from Federal forces. Belle Meade Mansion is a notable example of Greek Revival architecture with high ceilings and a lovely curving staircase. The Hermitage, home of Andrew Jackson, is 13 miles east. He died here in 1845 and the mansion is just as he left it—original furniture and Rachel Jackson's garden. The Parthenon is a full-size replica of the Parthenon on the Acropolis in Athens. It contains casts of the Elgin Marbles, 19th and 20th century art, and pre-Columbia artifacts. The State Capitol is a splendid building in Ionic Greek style, designed by William Strickland. Fort Nashborough is a smaller but authentic replica of the original fort established in 1779, when the settlers were attacked by Creeks and Cherokees. Visitors shouldn't miss the chance to ride the paddle-wheeler *Belle Carol* along the lovely Cumberland River.

ACCOMMODATIONS
Rates vary from $2.00 - $5.00 per person per day

MEALS
Information is not available.

ACTIVITIES (on campus or nearby)
Off campus: country music at Grand Ole Opry. Bus tours of Nashville: WSM Scenic Tours. Fishing, boating, water sports at nearby lakes.

AVAILABLE DATES
June 10 — September 10
Reservations are required.

CONTACT
Housing Office
3500 Centennial Boulevard
Telephone: (615) 329-9500

McMURRY COLLEGE
Abilene, Texas 79605

Abilene has grown from a frontier settlement with log
cabins to an important oil and gas center. The city is a
three hour ride by car from Fort Worth and Wichita.
Stop in to Old Abilene Town which is a faithful
reproduction of the old frontier village. Browse in the
shops for interesting nick-nacks and old-time foods.
Nearby is Burro Alley, a re-creation of a Mexican
village filled with shops and interesting exhibits. For
golfers, there is the Maxwell Municipal Golf Course. For
the outdoors lovers, there is camping, picnicking, water
sports, and swimming at Abilene State Park.

ACCOMMODATIONS
Single room — $3.00 per person per day
Double room — $3.00 per person per day
Suite (accommodating 4 persons) – $3.00 per person per day
Baths are shared. No linens or maid services are provided.
Pets and alcoholic beverages are not permitted.
Accommodations are available to students, prospective
matriculants, and youth groups.

MEALS
Cafeteria (typical prices)
Breakfast — $1.15
Lunch — $1.50
Dinner — $1.60
No meals are provided on weekends. A restaurant is
available off-campus.

ACTIVITIES (on campus or nearby)
Tennis courts. Gym facilities available for a fee.
Art museum, community theatre, and symphony
orchestra in Abilene.

AVAILABLE DATES
June 1 — August 15
Advance reservations required at least 2 weeks in advance.

CONTACT
Bill Phillips
Box 308
McMurry Station
Telephone: (915) 692-4130

BAUDER FASHION COLLEGE
Arlington, Texas 76010

Arlington and Grand Prairie are neighbor cities between Dallas and Fort Worth; practically suburbs of the latter two. In the area are some of the state's leading tourist attractions. Six Flags Over Texas is a unique entertainment center. Lion Country Safari offers self-guided tours of a wildlife reservation. Seven Seas is a sea-life park with variegated attractions. The Old West is recreated at the Southwestern Historical Wax Museum. And for avid sports fans, there may be a home game scheduled for the Texas Rangers.

ACCOMMODATIONS
Single room — $6.45 per person per day;
$45.15 per person per week
Double room — $4.95 per person per day;
$34.65 per person per week
Rates are subject to tax. Baths are shared. Pets and alcoholic beverages are not permitted.
Accommodations are available to students, alumni, adults, families and prospective matriculants.

MEALS
A cafeteria is available. Group rates are available.
```
 1 -  25 persons — $4.50 per person per day
26 -  50 persons — $4.00 per person per day
51 - 100 persons — $3.00 per person per day
```
Prices are subject to tax.

ACTIVITIES
Public activities nearby.

AVAILABLE DATES ·
June 5 — August 21
Advance reservations are required.

CONTACT
Miss Susan Huston
Public Relations
508 South Center Street
Telephone: (817) 277-6666

HENDERSON COUNTY JUNIOR COLLEGE
Athens, Texas 75751

Ranching and cattle breeding give Athens the atmosphere
of an old Texas frontier town. Athens is the Henderson
County seat. Dallas and Forth Worth are approximately
70 and 100 miles to the northwest, respectively.

ACCOMMODATIONS
Single room — $3.00 per person per day;
$15.00 per person per week
Pets and alcoholic beverages are not permitted.
Accommodations are available to students, alumni, adults,
families and prospective matriculants.

MEALS
Restaurants and coffee shops are nearby.

ACTIVITIES (on campus or nearby)
Tennis, handball, swimming, fishing and boating.
Cedar Creek Lake and Fort Parker are nearby.

AVAILABLE DATES
June 15 — August 3

CONTACT
Dr. William M. McMullen
Telephone: (214) 675-6213

TEXAS

NORTHWOOD INSTITUTE
Cedar Hills, Texas 75104

Cedar Hills is located just outside of Dallas on U.S. 67,
41 miles from Fort Worth. Unlike some other Texas cities,
Dallas has no tradition of invasions and battles or of
wild days when cattlemen, gamblers and outlaws
participated in lurid scenes of violence. Its prominence
as a center of business and commerce is rivalled by its
many cultural attractions and world-famous shops.
Dallas is known as a fashion center, as well as for
its theatres, museums and skyscrapers.

ACCOMMODATIONS
Single room — $12.00 per person per day;
$84.00 per person per week
Double room — $4.00 per person per day;
$28.00 per person per week
Apartment — $16.00 per person per day;
$112.00 per person per week
Baths are shared or private. Linens are $1.00 additional.
Alcoholic beverages are not permitted.
Accommodations are available to students, alumni, adults,
families and prospective matriculants.

MEALS
Cafeteria (typical prices)
Breakfast — $1.25
Lunch — $2.00
Dinner — $2.75

ACTIVITIES (on campus or nearby)
Approximately 15 miles from an amusement park and
the Dallas-Fort Worth Wax Museum, the State Fair Music
Hall, Fair Park Coliseum (ice skating). Dallas Black
Hawks ice hockey team plays in the fall and winter,
the Dallas Cowboys football team plays in the fall,
the Texas Rangers play in the spring and summer.
The State Fair takes place from September 16-30, and
the Cotton Bowl on January 1.

AVAILABLE DATES
Facilities are available all year round, however many
more units are available from May 3 through September 16.
Advance reservations are required.

CONTACT
Mr. Charles L. Morrison
P.O. Box 58
Telephone: (214) 291-1541

UNIVERSITY OF DALLAS
Irving, Texas 75061

Irving is just north of exciting Dallas, near Texas
Stadium, the home of the Dallas Cowboys. Several days
can be spent exploring all the attractions of the State
Fair Park, a 250-acre exposition site: the Music Hall,
where famous film and Broadway stars perform in
musicals; the Texas Sports Hall of Fame; the Aquarium
where you can watch the daily feeding of seals, reptiles
and fish; the Natural History Museum which focuses on
habitat groups of Southwestern animals; European and
American art, African sculpture, and ancient and
pre-Columbian art at the Museum of Fine Arts; the Age
of Steam Railroad Museum, with equipment dating from
the 1900's; a Health and Science Museum and Planetarium;
a midway with rides, concessions, picnic areas and cafe;
the Dallas Garden Center; the Cotton Bowl; the Texas
Hall of State, depicting the state's history and heroes.
Don't miss the Dallas Theatre Center, designed by
Frank Lloyd Wright, and the sculpture gardens in the
Market Center. There are hundreds of other attractions
in this handsome city, and an active nightlife.

ACCOMMODATIONS
Double room — $3.00 per person per day
No pets are permitted. No accommodations for married
people. Baths are shared.
Accommodations are available to students, alumni, adults.

MEALS
Cafeteria (typical prices)
Breakfast — $ .90
Lunch — ' $1.30
Dinner — $2.50

ACTIVITIES (on campus or nearby)
Pool, basketball, tennis.

AVAILABLE DATES
June 1 — mid-August
Reservations are required.

CONTACT
Brian Keller, Director of Housing
Box 73
Telephone: (214) 253-2121

UNIVERSITY OF UTAH
Salt Lake City, Utah 84110

Salt Lake is a beautiful city. Overlooked by mountains
to the east, it extends from its two main landmarks—the
handsome capitol and Temple Square—in ten-acre blocks,
with streets that are 132 feet wide and lined with trees.
Temple Square, headquarters of the Mormons, contains
the Tabernacle with a huge organ, where the famous
Tabernacle Choir may be heard during rehearsals; the
Assembly Hall; the Seagull Monument which com-
memorates the birds who saved the vital wheat crop from
the plague of crickets in the early settler days; and the
Old Log House, one of the settlement's first houses.
The Pioneer Village is interesting for its collection of
restored and furnished buildings dating from the city's
early history. Great Salt Lake is 17 miles to the west.
Here you can picnic and swim without fear of drowning—
its high salt content prevents bodies from sinking.

ACCOMMODATIONS
Single room—$6.00 per person per day
Double room—$5.00 per person per day
Apartments—$48.50 per week.
Baths are shared.
Accommodations are available to the general public.
However, small children will be accommodated only
in the apartments.

MEALS
Cafeteria (typical prices)
Breakfast — $1.50
Lunch — $2.00
Dinner — $2.50

ACTIVITIES (on campus or nearby)
Tennis, swimming, golf and bowling; Marriott Library
containing collection of Mormon memorabilia; Utah
Museums of Fine Arts and Natural History.

AVAILABLE DATES
July 1—August 16
Reservations are required.

CONTACT
Mrs. Newman
PO Box 200
Telephone: (801) 581-6483

ST. JOSEPH COLLEGE
Bennington, Vermont 05201

Bennington is in the southwestern corner of the state. It is from this point that the well-known scenic Molly Stark Trail to the east and the famous Long Trail to the north over the highest peaks of the principal Green Mountain ranges, begin. Situated on the New York frontier, Bennington became the focal point in the strife between the New Hampshire Grants and the "Yorkers" and was the background against which the opening scenes of Vermont history were enacted. The name of the town is most widely known in connection with the Battle of Bennington (1777) which lessened Burgoyne's dominance in the northern theatre of the Revolutionary War.

ACCOMMODATIONS
Single room — $7.00 per person per day;
$40.00 per person per week
Double room — $7.00 per person per day;
$40.00 per person per week
Baths are shared and private. Pets are not permitted. Accommodations are available to students, alumni, adults, families and prospective students.

MEALS
A cafeteria is available.

ACTIVITIES (on campus or nearby)
Community swimming pool, tennis courts, golf course and hiking trails are available. Special events include auctions and Bennington Battle Day.

AVAILABLE DATES
June 1 — August 31
Advance reservations are not required.

CONTACT
St. Joseph College
Monument Road
Telephone: (802) 442-5427

THE EXPERIMENT IN INTERNATIONAL LIVING
Brattleboro, Vermont 05301

Ten minutes from Brattleboro, headquarters of The Experiment and campus of its School for International Training, there's a unique emotional and cultural experience welcoming vacationers and travelers. It is the Alumni House, Himmel-on-the-Hill, a large Bavarian chalet nestled among hillside maples on 55 acres near the village of Putney. Brattleboro and Putney are Vermont at its picturesque best. Summer concerts and winter ski trails, informal musicales, ballet, international events and lectures, and various ethnic arts and skills are among wide-ranging cultural and recreational attractions.
Himmel — "heaven" in German — accommodates ten guests in rooms furnished from different countries. Their decor is, respectively, Vermont, Swedish, Mexican and Hungarian. Japanese living room, Italian dining room, and an Austrian farmer's living room in the cellar invite guests' use.

ACCOMMODATIONS
Single room — $8.00 per person per day
Double room — $6.00 per person per day
An adjoining single room for children under the age of 12 is $3.00 per night. The House has guest facilities for ten persons per night.
Baths are shared. Linens are included.
Accommodations are available to alumni, volunteers, hosts, students, families, Experiment friends, adults and prospective matriculants.

MEALS
Breakfast available on a self-service basis. Guests are invited to make use of house facilities and fully-equipped kitchen. Several fine inns and restaurants are nearby.

ACTIVITIES (on campus or nearby)
Woods, swimming pond, hiking, backpacking and skiing. Ski equipment is available for rent at all ski areas.

AVAILABLE DATES
Facilities are available all year round.

CONTACT
Mr. Stephen G. Barefoot
Public Relations, The Experiment
Telephone (802) 257-7751

TRINITY COLLEGE
Burlington, Vermont 05401

Lake Champlain is an exciting, scenic setting for
Burlington, Vermont's largest city. Industry and tourism
are both important to its economy. Winter skiers and
summer yachtsmen find that this area provides them
with excellent facilities. For history buffs, attractions
are Battery Park and Ethan Allan Park; for art lovers,
the Shelburne and Fleming Museums; and for theatre
enthusiasts, the Shakespeare Festival during the
month of August.

ACCOMMODATIONS
Single room — $6.00 per person per day
Double room — $5.00 per person per day
Baths are shared. Pets are not permitted.
Accommodations are available to students, alumni, adults,
families and prospective matriculants.

MEALS
Cafeteria (typical prices)

Breakfast —	$1.35	Special Dinners —	$2.50
Lunch —	$1.70	Dinner —	$2.25
Brunch —	$1.70		

ACTIVITIES (on campus or nearby)
Green Mountains offer mountain climbing and backpacking. Lake Champlain offers boating and swimming.
Nominal fees are charged for the public beach, golf and
tennis courts. Sporting equipment is available for rent.

AVAILABLE DATES
June 22 — August 23
Advance reservations are required.

CONTACT
Sister Ruth Ravey
Colchester Avenue
Telephone: (802) 658-0337, extension 339

NOVA (ANNANDALE CAMPUS)
Annandale, Virginia 22110

Annandale is a short distance from the nation's capital, Washington, D.C. and from the famous Manassas (Bull Run) National Battlefield Park. There are concerts and performances at the Kennedy Center in Washington, Wolf Trap Farm Park in Vienna, and in nearby Shady Grove Theatre and Capitol Center. At Manassas there's the Battlefield Museum with audio-visual presentations; the Stone Bridge where First Manassas began and where Federal troops retreated after Second Manassas; a battle line of the Civil War is preserved at the Unfinished Railroad; Dogan House and Stone House, each involved in both battles. The Skyline Drive and Caverns are less than an hour away.

ACCOMMODATIONS
Single room — $20.00 per person per week —
Fairview Rooming House, Manassas.
Three students can split an accommodation at the
All State Motel, Fairfax — $65.00 total per week.
Accommodations are available to students.

MEALS
Short-order and other eating facilities are in the area of the campus.

ACTIVITIES (on campus or nearby)
On campus: fishing on lake; tennis: no fee. Golf course nearby: no fee. Swimming in area: fee charged.

AVAILABLE DATES
Year round.
Reservations are required.

CONTACT
Kathleen M. Sullivan, Office Manager
Housing Referral Service
8333 Little River Turnpike
Telephone: (703) 323-3143

MARYMOUNT COLLEGE
Arlington, Virginia 22207

Arlington National Cemetery, here, originated in 1864
and is the nation's most famous national cemetery.
Presidents William Howard Taft and John F. Kennedy
are buried here. Take one of the tour buses to visit:
Tomb of the Unknown Soldier, Memorial Amphitheatre,
and Arlington House, the superb Greek Revival home of
Robert E. Lee The huge Iwo Jima statue, memorial to
the Marine Corps, is on Arlington Boulevard. Fairfax is
just a few miles from Arlington and should not be
missed. The entire town is an historical treasure.
Notable sites are: Fairfax Court House where George
and Martha Washington's wills are displayed; the Sully
Plantation, home of the brother of "Lighthouse" Harry
Lee, where you can see a log schoolhouse, an outdoor
kitchen-wash house, a stone house, lovely gardens and
the mansion itself. The Plantation holds crafts demonstrations during Plantation Days in mid-May. The
Manassas (Bull Run) National Battlefield Park, a short
distance from the college, the site of two major and bloody
battles of the Civil War. Don't miss the audio-visual
presentation of the battles at the Battlefield Museum.

ACCOMMODATIONS
Fees range from $4.00 to $8.00 per person per day
Accommodations are available to community, religious
and civic groups. Transients will be accommodated on
a space-available basis.

MEALS
Information is not available.

ACTIVITIES (on campus or nearby)
Off campus: Varied programs at Filene Center,
Wolftrap Farm Park; Plantation Days (Sully Plantation)
mid-May. Swimming, picnicking, boating, fishing, at local
lakes in Fairfax.

AVAILABLE DATES
Year round
Groups by advance reservation. Transients on a space-
available basis.

CONTACT
2607 North Olebe Road
Telephone: (703) 524-2500

FERRUM COLLEGE
Ferrum, Virginia 24088

Ferrum is in the heart of the Blue Ridge Mountains where the vacationer will view some of the finest scenery in the eastern United States. It is 12 miles east of the Blue Ridge Parkway and 35 miles southwest of Roanoke. The recreational and cultural activities of the area include arts and crafts, playhouses, recreational areas, numerous historical points and miles of trails. On or off the campus, there will never be enough time to enjoy it all.

ACCOMMODATIONS
Suite — $7.00 single; $11.00 double
Suite rates include private bath and program fee.
Apartments and special family rates available.
Linens are included.
Accommodations are available to students, alumni, adults, and families.

MEALS
Cafeteria (typical prices)
Breakfast — $1.50
Lunch — $1.75
Dinner — $2.00
A coffee shop is available.

ACTIVITIES (on campus or nearby)
Area attractions are the Blue Ridge Parkway, Smith Mountain Lake, Philpott Reservoir, Mill Mountain Playhouse, Fairystone State Park, Mill Mountain Children's Zoo, Roanoke Fine Arts Center, Booker T. Washington National Monument, Transportation Museum, and the Barn Dinner Theatre. Hiking, swimming, tennis, fishing and archery. There is a nominal charge for swimming and tennis lessons and horseback riding. Programs include arts and crafts classes and hiking trips. Fishing and archery equipment is available for rental.

AVAILABLE DATES
June 8 — August 16
Advance reservations required.

CONTACT
Director, Summer Program
Telephone: (703) 365-2121, extension 240

EASTERN MENNONITE COLLEGE
Harrisonburg, Virginia 22801

Harrisonburg is in the heart of the Shenandoah Valley
embraced by the beautiful rolling landscape. The George
Washington National Forest and the famous Skyline
Drive are nearby. In Harrisonburg, be sure to see the
Rockingham County Historical Society and the Revel B.
Pritchett Museum where interesting exhibitions on the
area and the Confederacy can be found. Within easy
driving distance are: The Natural Chimneys, a beautiful
natural phenomenon; the Shenandoah Caverns; and the
Senaca Rocks and Caverns. Charlottesville is about two
hours south of Harrisonburg. Here much of the Old South
is still quite evident. Ash Lawn, built in 1799, is the
mansion once belonging to James Monroe, (the country's
fifth president) named for the ash trees that are on the
front lawn. Much of the furniture and his belongings
are on display. Also in Charlottesville, is the Lewis
and Clark Memorial and the Michie Tavern.

ACCOMMODATIONS
Single room — $4.50 per person per day;
$30.00 per person per week
Double room — $4.00 per person per day;
$30.00 per person per week
Baths are shared. Linen service is provided. Pets,
smoking and alcoholic beverages are not permitted.
Accommodations are available to the general public.

MEALS
Breakfast — No rates available
Lunch — , $1.50
Dinner — $2.00

ACTIVITIES (on campus or nearby)
Hiking, tennis, archery, ping-pong, ski lift, golfing,
fishing and swimming.

AVAILABLE DATES
June 1 — September 1

CONTACT
Mrs. Frances Brubaker
Resident Director
Telephone: (703) 433-2771

OLD DOMINION UNIVERSITY
Norfolk, Virginia 23508

Getting to Norfolk, one of the East Coast's finest harbors and recreation areas, becomes an exciting trip via the Chesapeake Bay Bridge-Tunnel to Cape Charles. Norfolk harbor is one of the finest in the world, an exciting boat tour along with the Naval Shipyard across the Elizabeth River. Within a short drive are Cape Henry and Virginia Beach, Colonial Williamsburg, Jamestown Colony and the Seashore State Park. Art lovers wil enjoy the fascinating collections of the Chrysler Museum and the Heritage Foundation Museum. Norfolk Gardens-by-the-Sea not only is a botanical attraction, but also includes boat and train tours and a replica of a pirate ship.

ACCOMMODATIONS
Single room—$6.00 per person per day;
$42.00 per person per week
Double occupancy—$10.00 per day;
Family suite—$12.00 per day; $84.00 per week
Baths are private. Pets are not permitted.
Accommodations are available to students, alumni, adults, families and prospective matriculants.

MEALS
Cafeteria (typical prices)
Breakfast — $1.00
Lunch — $1.50
Dinner — $2.00

ACTIVITIES (on campus or nearby)
Swimming, tennis, boating, beaching, horseback riding and fishing. Thoroughgood House and Civil War Plantations, and Yorktown are within easy driving distance.

AVAILABLE DATES
May 17—August 17
Advance reservations are not required.

CONTACT
Mr. James L. Guion Jr.
General Manager
Rogers-Gresham Halls
Telephone: (804) 489-6696

EASTERN WASHINGTON STATE COLLEGE
Cheney, Washington 99004

Cheney, 16 miles from Spokane and about 37 miles from the Idaho border, is located in lake country—50 lakes within 50 miles—on the edge of the vast, rich mining and lumbering areas of Idaho and Montana. The college contains the Gallery of Art which holds the free Artist and Lecture series, and the College Theatre. In nearby Spokane, there is highly varied nighttime entertainment; the Japanese and Duncan gardens; "Walk in the Wild" zoo; the Cheney-Cowles Museum; the Pacific Northwest Indian Center; the park and cultural Expo Center; a civic theatre and symphony. Rodeos are held almost every weekend in nearby towns as well as local festivals and flower shows. A pleasant day's round trip takes you to Grand Coulee Dam.

ACCOMMODATIONS
Single room—$7.00 per person per day
Double room—$5.00 per person per day
All rooms contain two single beds. Bathroom and shower facilities are centrally located. Bed linens, only, are provided. Pets and alcoholic beverages are not permitted. No cots, cribs, etc. are permitted.
Accommodations are available to the general public.

MEALS
Cafeteria (typical prices)
Breakfast — $1.50
Lunch — $1.75
Dinner — $2.50

ACTIVITIES (on campus or nearby)
On campus: swimming and tennis—no charge. Off campus: fishing, boating, golfing—fees vary. Hiking and mountain climbing: professional and hiking clubs available. Equipment rental available through commercial outlets.

AVAILABLE DATES
Mid-June—Mid-September
Reservations are required.

CONTACT
Isabelle Green
Coordinator, Workshop's Conferences
Showalter 308A
Telephone: (509) 359-2275

SAINT MARTIN'S COLLEGE
Olympia, Washington 98503

Olympia, the capital of Washington State, is a beautifully maintained, park-like community at the southern end of Puget Sound. Low green hills surround it, framed by Mt. Rainier and the Olympics. This is a seaport town with a mild climate. Local recreation includes nearby lakes for boating, fishing and swimming, salt water sports and golf. The 550-acre campus is near Pacific Ocean beaches, the Olympic and Cascade Mountain Ranges, Olympic National Park, and several Indian reservations. The capital buildings and grounds, featuring seasonal plantings and Japanese cherry trees are a mecca for visitors.

ACCOMMODATIONS
Single room — $5.00 per person per day;
$32.00 per person per week
Double room — $4.00 per person per day;
$25.00 per person per week
Baths are shared. Pets are not permitted.
Accommodations are available to students, alumni, adults, families and prospective matriculants.

MEALS
Cafeteria (typical prices)
Breakfast — $1.25
Lunch — $1.50
Dinner — $1.75

ACTIVITIES (on campus or nearby)
Swimming, fishing, tennis, hiking, boating and mountain sports. A gymnasium is on campus.

AVAILABLE DATES
June 1 — August 15
Advance reservations are required.

CONTACT
Business Manager's Office
700 College Way
Telephone: (206) 491-4700

WASHINGTON STATE UNIVERSITY
Pullman, Washington 99163

Pullman is named for the inventor whose name was also given to the railroad sleeping car. The city, in the fertile Palouse Hills, is a major storage and shipping center, midway between Spokane and Walla Walla. The campus provides summer theatre and band performances at the Summer Palace. Also on campus is a small but excellent natural history museum, the Charles R. Conner Museum. A few miles away is Chief Kamiakin State Park where you can hike on marked trails and picnic. About 20 miles away is Moscow, Idaho, in the lovely Paradise Valley. While here, visit the old Fort Russell site, which marks the area where settlers gathered for refuge against the attack by Chief Joseph and the Nez Perce in 1877.

ACCOMMODATIONS
Single room — $3.00 - $6.00 per person per day
Double room — $3.00 - $8.00 per day
The maximum stay is 75 days.
Accommodations are available to students.

MEALS
Information is not available.

ACTIVITIES (on campus or nearby)
On campus: summer theatre from late June to mid-August. Off campus: hiking, camping, picnicking.

AVAILABLE DATES
June 15 — September 1
Reservations are suggested.

CONTACT
Housing Officer
Telephone: (509) 335-4577

SEATTLE PACIFIC COLLEGE
Seattle, Washington 98119

Urban Seattle, center of a metropolitan area with a population over 860,000, located on Puget Sound, still retains the flavor of the Alaskan gold rush, fur trapping, and timber booms for which it was the trading center. It is still a major port for trade with Alaska and the Far East, and the commercial, industrial and financial center of the Pacific Northwest. Situated on a series of hills above a fine harbor, it is surrounded by great natural beauty. West of Puget Sound are the Olympic Mountains, dominated by Mt. Olympus. The eastern boundary of the city is 26-mile long Lake Washington, backed by the Cascade range. To the south rises snow-capped Mount Rainier. Northward is the Canadian port of Vancouver, entry to Banff, Lake Louise and Cascade National Park. The area is considered the most spectacular recreational and sight-seeing country in the Western Hemisphere.

ACCOMMODATIONS
Single room — $7.00 per person per day;
$48.00 per person per week
Double room — $5.50 per person per day;
$38.00 per person per week
Baths are shared. Linens and maid service are included. Pets, smoking, and alcoholic beverages are not permitted. Accommodations are available to students, alumni, and prospective matriculants.

MEALS
Cafeteria (typical prices)
Breakfast — $1.75
Lunch — $2.50
Dinner — $3.75
A coffee shop is available.

ACTIVITIES (on campus or nearby)
Seattle Pacific College summer Festival, Seattle Center, Pioneer Square, Underground Seattle, Space Needle and Rain Forest.

AVAILABLE DATES
June 15 — September 1
Advance reservations are required.

CONTACT
Mr. Robert Jorgensen
Director of Public Relations
Telephone: (206) 281-2051

SEATTLE UNIVERSITY
Seattle, Washington 98122

Urban Seattle, center of a metropolitan area with a population over one and one-half million, located on Puget Sound, still retains the flavor of Pioneer Seattle. It's still a major port for trade with Alaska and the Far East, and the commercial, industrial and financial center of the Pacific Northwest. Situated on a series of hills above a fine harbor, it is surrounded by great natural beauty. West of Puget Sound are the Olympic Mountains, dominated by Mt. Olympus. The eastern boundary of the city is 26-mile long Lake Washington, backed by the Cascade range. To the south rises snow-capped Mount Rainier. Northward is the Canadian port of Vancouver. The fair grounds from the World's Fair of 1962 are still preserved (Pacific Science Center, Space Needle, monorail, etc.) Other highlights which make Seattle are its U.S. Government Locks, the Washington State Ferry System, the Public Market, and Pioneer Square in the heart of Old Seattle.

ACCOMMODATIONS
Single room — $7.00 per person per day;
$49.00 per person per week; $100.00 per person per month
Double room — $4.50 per person per day;
$31.50 per person per week; $75.00 per person per month
Baths are shared. Pets, children and alcoholic beverages are not permitted.
Accommodations are available to students and adults.

MEALS
Cafeteria (typical prices)
Breakfast — $1.10
Lunch — $1.50
Dinner — $2.00

ACTIVITIES (on campus or nearby)
Tennis, squash, swimming, canoeing, hiking, bicycling, skiing, mountain climbing, boating and fishing.

AVAILABLE DATES
Facilities are available all year round.
Advance reservations are required.

CONTACT
Bernie Carvalho
Campion Tower
914 E. Jefferson
Telephone: (206) 626-5638

FORT WRIGHT COLLEGE
Spokane, Washington 99204

Located at the falls of the Spokane River and
50 miles from its mouth in the Columbia River, Spokane
is surrounded by pine-clad mountains, rivers,
cascades, waterfalls, lakes, orchards and fertile grain
fields. It is protected by mountain ranges from extremes
of heat and cold and from the fogs of the coast. There is a
choice of 76 lakes for picnics, swimming, boating, and
fishing—reaching from Coulee Dam National Recreation
Area to the north to the spectacular Coeur d'Alene
National Forest to the east.

ACCOMMODATIONS
Single room—$5.00 per person per day;
$35.00 per person per week
Double room—$5.00 per person per day;
$35.00 per person per week
Baths are shared. Pets and children are not permitted.
Accommodations are available to adults and prospective
matriculants.

MEALS
Cafeteria (typical prices)
Breakfast — $1.00
Lunch — $1.35
Dinner — $1.75

ACTIVITIES (on campus or nearby)
Tennis, water sports, hiking and bicycling.

AVAILABLE DATES
June 1—August 15
Advance reservations are required.

CONTACT
Director of Housing
Telephone: (509) 328-2970, extension 78

GONZAGA UNIVERSITY
Spokane, Washington 99202

Because of the surrounding mountains, Spokane is blessed with warm, dry winters and summers that resemble those of Maine. It's set in a lovely valley and the Spokane River flows through its midst. The city is a delightful place to visit: bustling, good-natured, handsome. The Cathedral of St. John the Evangelist is a Gothic structure with lovely stone and wood carvings and stained glass. There are art exhibits, natural history dioramas, Indian arts and crafts, and pioneer relics at the Historical Society museums, and an old steam locomotive at High Bridge Park. The splendid Spokane Falls and the river's cascades, illuminated at night, may be seen from the Monroe Street Birdge. The campus itself contains the Crosby Library, donated by Bing Crosby, which contains some of the singer's, memorabilia. Cliff Park, built around a volcanic island, offers a panoramic view of the city and the area.

ACCOMMODATIONS
Single room — $4.00 - $9.00 per person per night
Double room — $7.00 - $20.00 per night
Special group rates are available.
Accommodations are available to the general public.

MEALS
Information is not available.

ACTIVITIES (on campus or nearby)
Fishing, motor bike trails, picnicking, swimming, bridle paths are available at local parks. Golfing at municipal courses. Lilac Festival in mid-May: parades, flower show, concert and exhibits. Horse racing at Playfair Race Course.

AVAILABLE DATES
May 15 — August 27
Reservations are required.

CONTACT
Housing Officer
E. 502 Boone Avenue
Telephone: (509) 328-4220

CONCORD COLLEGE
Athens, West Virginia 24712

Athens is a small and relaxed town nestled in the
Applachian Mountains. Within easy reach are the cities
of Bluefield and Princeton. Bluefield got its name for the
lovely blue chicory that covers the surrounding hills.
It also has the sobriquet: "the air-conditioned city"
because it is a half-mile above sea level and thus has a
cool, enjoyable atmosphere. Tours are available in the
Pocahontas Exhibition Mine. Pinnacle Rock State Park
should be seen for the amazing half-mile long sandstone
formation that resembles a giant cockscomb. Be sure to
take a few hours to enjoy Skyland with its: "Ridge
Runner" Railroad, said to be the shortest railroad in the
world; The Museum of the Hills, and the Mountain
Crafts Shop. In Princeton, the 5,897 acres of Camp Creek
State Forest has picnicking, fishing, hunting, playground,
game courts, and camp grounds for its visitors.

ACCOMMODATIONS
Single room — $6.00 per person per day;
$42.00 per person per week
Double room — $4.50 per person per day;
$31.50 per person per week
Student rates:
Single room — $3.50 per person per day;
$24.00 per person per week
Double room — Same as single room rates
Baths are shared. Linen service available for 25¢. Maid
service for $3.00. No pets or liquor over beer alcoholic
content are allowed.
Accommodations are available to students, alumni,
and prospective matriculants.

MEALS
Cafeteria (typical prices)
Breakfast — $1.15
Lunch — $1.45
Dinner — $1.70

ACTIVITIES (on campus or nearby)
Swimming pool, handball courts, tennis, paddle ball,
billiards, and bowling. A $1.00 fee will cover all.

AVAILABLE DATES
Facilities are available year round.
Reservations are suggested.

CONTACT
Director of Housing and Residential Life
Telephone: (304) 384-3115

WEST VIRGINIA WESLEYAN COLLEGE
Buckhannon, West Virginia 26201

This lovely 78-acre campus holds the Wesley Chapel which contains the twelve disciple sculptures of Wolfgang Flor and a handsome pink marble altar piece. There's an interesting and varied Strawberry Festival in early June in Buckhannon. Outdoor activities, including swimming in a mountain pool, are available at a nearby park. The campus is in the beautiful Appalachians, near many forests and parks. A glassware factory in nearby Weston offers tours to visitors. The Bowden National Fish Hatchery, an interesting spot, is 10 miles east of Elkins.

ACCOMMODATIONS
Rates vary from $5.00 to $7.00 per person per day. Accommodations are open to the general public.

MEALS
Information is not available.

ACTIVITIES (on campus or nearby)
Off campus: hiking, swimming, outdoor activities at Audra State Park. Strawberry Festival (arts and crafts, air show, parades, ball, dances, etc.) — early June.

AVAILABLE DATES
June 1 — August 30
Reservations are required.

CONTACT
Housing Office
Telephone: (304) 473-8485

MARSHALL UNIVERSITY
Huntington, West Virginia 25701

Huntington was founded in 1871 by the millionaire president of the Chesapeake and Ohio Railroad, Collis P. Huntington. Huntington is now the largest city in the state, precisely planned and protected from the Ohio River by an 11 mile flood wall, 17 pumping stations and 45 gates. On the campus a Geology Museum and Shakespeare Room are free of charge. While touring Huntington, take the free Industrial Tours offered by the Rainbow Art Glass Co., Blenko Glass Co., and the Pilgrim Glass Corp. where you can watch craftsmen make handblown glass. There are many interesting displays in the gift shops. Huntington has more than 1,000 acres of parks offering fun and relaxation any time of the day. Take a few hours to go to the Huntington Galleries which is known for its 18th, 19th, and 20th-century American and European paintings and sculptures; Herman Dean Arms Collection, Georgian silver, contemporary mountain arts and crafts. Classes and concerts are also held on a regular basis.

ACCOMMODATIONS
Single room—$6.00 per person per day
Double room—$5.00 per person per day
Apartments accommodating 4 people for $15.00 per night.
Private and shared baths. Linen service for $1.25.
No pets or alcoholic beverages are permitted.
Accommodations available to students, alumni, adults, families, small children, and prospective matriculants.

MEALS
Cafeteria (typical prices)
Breakfast — $1.05
Lunch — $1.25
Dinner — $1.75
Snack bars and restaurants are located on and off campus.

ACTIVITIES (on campus or nearby)
Just about any type of recreational facility available.

AVAILABLE DATES
Facilities are available all year round. Reservations are required.

CONTACT
Director of Housing
Old Main 126
Telephone: (304) 696-6765

WEST VIRGINIA STATE COLLEGE
Institute, West Virginia 25112

Just west of Charleston, West Virginia's state capital, Institute is in the rolling country of the Allegheny Plateau. Local arts and crafts are of major interest in this part of the country. Nearby, in Milton, is one of the major sources of hand-blown cathedral glass used in stained-glass windows. Readily accessible from Institute are many of West Virginia's natural attractions for outdoor recreation, hiking, boating and swimming and horseback riding.

ACCOMMODATIONS
Single room — $8.24 per person per day;
$57.68 per person per week
Double room — $5.15 per person per day;
$36.05 per person per week
Baths are shared. Rooms are air conditioned.
Accommodations are available to students, alumni, adults, families and prospective matriculants.

MEALS
Cafeteria (typical prices)
Breakfast — $1.00
Lunch — $1.25
Dinner — $1.75
A coffee shop is available.

ACTIVITIES (on campus or nearby)
Swimming, fishing, tennis, hiking, golf, boating and horseback riding.

AVAILABLE DATES
June 10 — August 10
Advance reservations are not required.

CONTACT
Mr. Charles L. Madison
Telephone: (304) 766-3140 or (304) 766-3149

WHEELING COLLEGE
Wheeling, West Virginia 26003

Wheeling is the manufacturing and commercial center of the Northern Panhandle. It spreads T-shaped along the narrow valleys of the Ohio River and Wheeling Creek, between and over a series of sharp rolling hills and across Wheeling Island in the Ohio River. Industrial development has attracted many immigrants from Europe — Germans, Italians, Poles, Russians, and Greeks, all having their own churches and fraternal societies. This gives the city a cosmopolitan atmosphere more akin to metropolitan areas than the other more leisurely-paced cities of West Virginia. Points of interest include Oglebay Park, one of the most outstanding, intensively used and developed in the United States, Historic Mansion House, Frontier Travel Gallery and Wheeling Park.

ACCOMMODATIONS
Single room — $6.00 per person per day;
$42.00 per person per week
Double room — $4.00 per person per day;
$28.00 per person per week
Rates are subject to a 3 per cent tax.
Accommodations are available to general public.
Pets are not permitted.

MEALS
Cafeteria (typical prices)
Breakfast — $1.50
Lunch — $2.00
Dinner — $2.50
Prices are subject to a 3 per cent tax.

ACTIVITIES (on campus or nearby)
Basketball, tennis, softball, golf, hiking, water sports and outdoor amphitheater.

AVAILABLE DATES
May 15 — September 1
Advance reservations are suggested.

CONTACT
Mrs. Arlene Houser
Director of Public Relations
Washington Avenue
Telephone: (304) 243-2295

BAY APARTMENTS — UNIVERSITY OF WISCONSIN
Green Bay, Wisconsin 54301

Green Bay has been an important trade center since 1669. It's the state's oldest city and is the home of the Packers football team. The Bay Beach Park and Wildlife Sanctuary provides children's fishing in the lagoons, nature trails, concessions, midway, rides, picnicking, entertainment and wading pool. There are shows and sports events at the Veteran Memorial Arena, as well as the Green Bay Packer Hall of Fame Museum. The National Railroad Museum houses steam engines and cars and you can ride either on a narrow-gauge miniature train or in antique coaches pulled by a standard-gauge steam locomotive. The Roi-Porlier-Tank Cottage is the oldest home in Wisconsin, furnished with period pieces. Memorabilia of early Fort Howard and Green Bay are housed in the Fort Howard Hospital Museum. There's golf at Shorewood (on campus) and at the County Course; swimming at nearby parks; picnicking at Lost Dauphine State Park.

ACCOMMODATIONS
2-bedroom completely furnished apartments — $3.25 per person per night.
Pets are not permitted. Baths are private. Linens: $1.50 per set.
Accommodations are available to the general public.

MEALS
A cafeteria and snack bar are on campus.

ACTIVITIES (on campus or nearby)
Biking, tennis, golf — about $2.00 per 9 holes.

AVAILABLE DATES
Year round. However, facilities are limited during the school year. Reservations are suggested.

CONTACT
Tim Gleason, Resident Manager
105-A1 Wasserman Lane
Telephone: (414) 465-0374

MILWAUKEE SCHOOL OF ENGINEERING
Milwaukee, Wisconsin 53201

Milwaukee, the metropolis on Lake Michigan, is the largest city of Wisconsin; a port of entry and county seat. Three rivers cut it into natural divisions, the east, the west, and the south sides. A large part of the lake front is owned by the city and developed in parks, airport and harbor facilities. The Botanical Gardens and Zoological Park are particularly outstanding and should not be missed. For a leisurely trip across Lake Michigan, take one of the many ferries, you don't have to take your car.

ACCOMMODATIONS
Single room — $3.50 per person per day;
$21.00 per person per week
Double room — $3.50 per person per day;
$17.00 per person per week
Baths are shared. Pets are not permitted.
Accommodations are available to students, alumni, adults and prospective matriculants.

MEALS
Restaurants and coffee shops are available.

ACTIVITIES (on campus or nearby)
Student center and exercise room are available. Programs include Old Milwaukee Days and Summerfest. Bradford Beach, the Performing Arts Center, and the Port of Milwaukee are in-town attractions.

AVAILABLE DATES
June 1 — August 20
Advance reservations are not required.

CONTACT
Director of Housing
1121 North Milwaukee Street
Telephone: (414) 272-8720

UNIVERSITY OF WISCONSIN
Milwaukee, Wisconsin 53201

Settled in the early 1800's by the English, Milwaukee
has long been famed for its progressive city government.
The St. Lawrence Seaway and Milwaukee's position on
Lake Michigan have played strategic roles in its emergence
as a major seaport. This city is a leader in the manufacture of electric power equipment, diesel and gasoline
engines and motors. Beer, of course, is a world renowned
export and familiarly known to all Americans. Very much
an industrial and metropolitan center, Milwaukee also
combines its versatility with a Performing Arts Center,
art exhibits, museums and theatre. The Great Lakes lend
to their bordering states a wealth of sports, fishing and
outdoor activities four seasons a year.

ACCOMMODATIONS
Private room with private bath — $11.00 per person
per night
Private room with private bath — $13.00 for a
married couple per night
Children (with parents) — $2.00 per child per night
Three persons per suite (private room, shared bath) —
$9.00 per person per night
Four to five persons per suite — $7.00 per person per night
All rooms are in suites consisting of three rooms with
private baths. There is an additional 4% sales tax charge
on all room fees.
Accommodations are available to students, alumni,
prospective matriculants and families.

MEALS
Cafeteria (typical prices)
Breakfast — $1.00
Lunch — $1.50
Dinner — $2.00
A coffee shop is available.

ACTIVITIES (on campus or nearby)
Swimming, boating, tennis, fishing and golf.
Old Milwaukee Days take place from June 30 to July 5,
and Summerfest is from July 12 to 22.

AVAILABLE DATES
May 19 — August 25
Advance reservations are not required.

CONTACT
Mr. Robert T. Seay, Conference Coordinator
3400 North Maryland Avenue
Telephone: (414) 963-4070

WISCONSIN

LAKELAND COLLEGE
Sheboygan, Wisconsin 53081

A commercial center for surrounding dairy farms famous for their excellent cheese, Sheboygan plays an important role as one of the eight largest harbor cities of Lake Michigan. It is also near Green Bay and Lake Winnebago. The city offers sporting activities at Kohler State Park, art showings at Kohler Arts Center, and historical exhibits at Sheboygan County Museum.

ACCOMMODATIONS
Single room—$5.80 per person per day (1974 rates. 1975 rates will rise: further information is not available) Linens are included. Pets are not permitted.
Accommodations are available to students, alumni, adults, families and prospective matriculants.

MEALS
Cafeteria (typical prices)
Breakfast — $1.00
Lunch — $1.30
Dinner— $2.05
A coffee shop is available.

ACTIVITIES (on campus or nearby)
Theater, sports, movies, coffee houses, tennis, game room, swimming and fishing. No fees are charged for sports activities.

AVAILABLE DATES
June 1—August 30
Advance reservations are required.

CONTACT
Mr. Richard C. Preuhs
Campus Center Director
Telephone: (414) 565-1227

CARROLL COLLEGE
Waukesha, Wisconsin 53186

Waukesha means "By the Little Fox," and the town was named for the river which runs through it. It is a quiet, gracious college town with a symphony orchestra. Waukesha was famed for its mineral springs and was one of the country's most fashionable spas in the last half of the 19th century. Prior to the Civil War it was an important station in the Underground Railroad. The Historical Museum here houses exhibits of county history. Midtown Milwaukee is about 15 miles away. Milwaukee is the world's major producer of beer and is a convivial, lively place with professional and college basketball, major league baseball, car racing, polo and soccer. On Milwaukee's beautiful lakefront are the Art Center, the Villa Terrace Decorative Arts Museum, the Yacht Club, and Bradford Beat with excellent swimming.

ACCOMMODATIONS
Prices range from $1.00 to $2.00 per person per night, depending on accommodations.
Children are not accommodated.
Accommodations are available to adults.

MEALS
Information is not available.

ACTIVITIES (on campus or nearby)
Off campus: golf, tennis, swimming, sailing, fishing, hiking, winter sports.

AVAILABLE DATES
September 10 — May 15
Reservations are suggested.

CONTACT
Housing Office
120 McCall Street
Telephone: (414) 547-9654

GEORGE WILLIAMS COLLEGE
Williams Bay, Wisconsin 53191

Williams Bay is on Lake Geneva, about an hour's drive from Racine and Kenosha, in the lovely area near Lake Michigan. While here, visit the Yerkes Asrtonomical Observatory which contains a 40-inch refracting telescope and astronomical exhibits. There are 49 parks in and around Racine, where you can picnic, and the Zoological Park which has a large animal collection and facilities for swimming and winter ice skating. Its Museum of Fine Arts has an extensive collection, and the Historical Museum provides changing exhibits of county history. Kenosha is a pretty city, fronting on Lake Michigan. Here is the international headquarters for the Barber Shop Quartet Singing Society, with a large library of Gay 90's and pop music. There's golfing in the county park and an industrial tour is possible at the American Motor Corporation.

ACCOMMODATIONS
Fees vary from $12 - $18 per person per day
Meals are included in the fee. Minimum stay: two days.
Accommodations are available to the general public.

MEALS
Included in the fee.

ACTIVITIES (on campus or nearby)
Winter and summer water sports.

AVAILABLE DATES
Year round
Reservations are required.

CONTACT
Housing Office
350 N. Lakeshore Drive
Telephone: (414) 245-5531

NORTHWEST COMMUNITY COLLEGE
Powell, Wyoming 82435

Northwest Community College is a two-year college offering a transfer program. The surroundings contribute to its growth and the enthusiasm of its students. Powell is a pleasant, clean agricultural town. It is just 23 miles from Cody, Wyoming, the east gateway to Yellowstone Park, and is surrounded on three sides by mountains offering a variety of outdoor recreation. Horseshoe Bend, in the Big Horn Recreation Area is just 35 miles away.

ACCOMMODATIONS
Double room — $1.75 per person per day;
$12.25 per person per week
Pets, alcoholic beverages and illegal drugs are not permitted. Baths are shared. Linens provided for a fee: $1.00 per night.
Accommodations are available to prospective matriculants.

MEALS
There is a restaurant off campus.

ACTIVITIES (on campus or nearby)
Hiking, outdoor recreation.

AVAILABLE DATES
May 25 — August 15
Reservations are required.

CONTACT
Mrs. K. Christiansen, Housing Director
Telephone: (307) 754-5151

UNIVERSITY OF CALGARY
Calgary, Alberta, Canada

Calgary is located on the Trans-Canada Highway in southern Alberta. Since 1947, when Leduc oil field was brought in, Calgary has become another Dallas or Houston. The Hospitality Center in the city introduces the many local attractions, among which are the Dinosaur Park and Zoo. Banff, 80 miles to the west in the Canadian Rockies, is the headquarters town of the exciting Banff National Park. A drive to Lake Louise is a must. Three-fifths of the province is forest—moose, caribou, buffalo and elk country. The marsh areas are among the greatest duck breeding locales in North America, where Indians gather wild rice for gourmets.

ACCOMMODATIONS
Single room — $9.00 per person per day;
$63.00 per person per week
Double room — $6.00 per person per day;
$42.00 per person per week
Youth rate — $5.00 per night, double occupancy only
Pets are not permitted. Conference facilities are available.
Accommodations are available to students, alumni, adults, families and prospective matriculants.

MEALS
Cafeteria (typical prices)
Breakfast — $1.50
Lunch — $1.75
Dinner — $2.25
A coffee shop is available.

ACTIVITIES (on campus or nearby)
Hiking, swimming and golf. There is a nominal charge for swimming. Calgary Stampede, July 6-14, Calgary Zoo (largest in Canada), Heritage Park, Glenbow Museum, Canadian Rockies (80 miles away), Lake Louise and numerous golf courses.

AVAILABLE DATES
May 1 — August 25
Advance reservations are preferred.

CONTACT
Mr. E. J. Sullivan
Food and Housing Special Functions Coordinator
2920 24th Avenue, Northwest
Telephone: (403) 284-6971

BRANDON UNIVERSITY
Brandon, Manitoba, Canada

Brandon is an important trading center on the trans-Canadian highway, in the southwestern part of the granary province of Manitoba. Not far from town is the Experimental Farm and directly south on Highway 10 is the International Peace Garden. To the north on Highway 10 is Riding Mountain National Park with its water sports, camping and hiking facilities.

ACCOMMODATIONS
Single room — $6.00 per person per day;
$42.00 per person per week
Double room — $6.00 per person per day;
$42.00 per person per week
Suite — $15.00 per person per day;
$105.00 per person per week
Baths are shared. Maid service is $1.00 additional.
Pets are not permitted.
Accommodations are available to students, alumni, adults, families and prospective matriculants.

MEALS
Cafeteria (typical prices)
Breakfast — $1.00
Lunch — $1.50
Dinner — $1.70

ACTIVITIES (on campus or nearby)
Swimming, hiking, golf, tennis, fishing and boating.
A fishing license is required. Guided tours are available.

AVAILABLE DATES
May 15 — August 30
Advance reservations are required.

CONTACT
Mr. A. R. McTaggart
Telephone: (204) 728-9520, extension 301

SAINT MARY'S UNIVERSITY
Halifax, Nova Scotia, Canada

CANADA

Staying at St. Mary's University is comparable to that
of a fashionable resort. Spacious, well-designed rooms,
modern conference rooms, games and music listening
rooms, a beauty salon, a barber shop, and a stadium are
some of the facilities provided for the welcomed visitor.
Some of the interesting things to see are: The QUASAR
3C-273, a celestial object estimated to be 1 billion,
300 million light years away; The Bedford Basin, with
panoramic views form the MacDonald and Mackay
Bridges; The Old Dutch Church built in 1756; the Point
Pleasant Park has golf, nature trails, beaches, and
historical sights; The Province House, a beautiful example
of Georgian architecture completed in 1818; the Public
Gardens; and the Scotia Square, 19 acres of partially
completed shopping, living, and business complex with
more than 60 stores now open to the public.

ACCOMMODATIONS
Single room—$7.00 per person per day
$35.00 per person per week
Double room—$6.00 per person per day
$30.00 per person per week
Furnished apartments accommodating 4 people available
for $25.00 per day; $125.00 per week.
Baths are shared. Linen service available with deposit.
Maid service provided for a fee.
Accommodations available to general public.

MEALS
Cafeteria (typical prices)
Breakfast — $1.50
Lunch — $1.50
Dinner — $2.00

ACTIVITIES (on campus or nearby)
May 1 - September 1—swimming, skating, tennis, games
room available on campus. Full recreational facilities
available in and around the city of Halifax.

AVAILABLE DATES
May 1—September 1
Reservations are suggested.

CONTACT
Director of University Residences
Telephone: (902) 422-7361

UNIVERSITY OF GUELPH
Guelph, Ontario, Canada

Guelph, located on the peninsula surrounded by Lakes
Ontario and Erie and the Georgian Bay, is ideal for the
enjoyment of water sports and outdoor recreation.
The cities of Hamilton, Toronto and London are within a
one hour drive. Guelph's history is embedded in the
architecture of the main street buildings—they are all
made of native gray limestone. A 44 foot living floral clock
in Riverside Park actually tells the time. Another architectural landmark is the gothic church of Our Lady of
Immaculate Conception made of native gray limestone.
A park borders the canyon of Elora Gorge, 20 minutes
from town.

ACCOMMODATIONS
Single room—$9.00 per person per day
Double room—$7.00 per person per day
Suite—$10.00 to $15.00 per day
Baths are shared. Linens and maid service are included.
Pets are not permitted.
Accommodations are available to students, alumni, adults,
families and prospective matriculants.

MEALS
Meals are sold on a "cash a la carte" basis. A number of
cafeterias and coffee shops are available on campus.

ACTIVITIES (on campus or nearby)
Facilities for all sports are available on campus. Nominal
fees are charged for swimming and tennis. Antique,
pottery and craft stores abound. Weekend trips and guided
scenic tours are available and are arranged by the
conference office at the university. Kortwright Waterfoul
Park, Elora Gorge and Rockwood Conservation Area are
nearby. The Stratford Shakespearean Festival takes
place from June to October.

AVAILABLE DATES
May 2—August 22
Advance reservations are required.

CONTACT
Mr. W. R. Jarrett, Assistant Director
Central Reservations and Conferences
Telephone: (519) 824-4120, extension 2638

CARLETON UNIVERSITY
Ottawa, Ontario, Canada

Archetypical in its architecture of what a nation's capital should look like, the city of Ottawa is on the Ottawa River which divides Quebec and Ontario Provinces. Visually exciting, the city blends its British and Canadian heritages to allow the visitor a sampling of the old and the new. The Parliament Buildings are the center of historic interest, the oldest having been constructed a little over 100 years ago, and the newest 57 years ago. The National Arts Centre is a showcase for Ottawa's avant-garde theatre and performing arts. Canada's artists are well represented at the National Gallery of Canada. Bi-cultural Quebec Province offers superb French cuisine, good skiing and many historical sites. The Laurentians offer mountain climbing, backpacking, skiing and just simply walking.

ACCOMMODATIONS
One night—$5.90 per person (room and breakfast)
Two nights or more—$5.15 per person/night
(room and breakfast)
These rates are subject to the assessment of an additional 3% sales tax. Baths are shared. Linens are included. Pets are not permitted.
Accommodations are available to groups only.

MEALS
Cafeteria (typical prices)
Lunch — $1.90
Box Lunch — $1.50
Dinner — $2.50

ACTIVITIES (on campus or nearby)
A pool, gymnasium and squash courts are available on campus. The Tulip Festival takes place in mid-May; the Highland Games, the first of July; and Festival Canada, the month of July.

AVAILABLE DATES
Mid-May—late August
Reservations are required at least four to six weeks in advance.

CONTACT
Mr. David Sterritt
Assistant Director
Student Housing and Food Services
Telephone: (613) 231-3610

UNIVERSITY OF OTTAWA
Ottawa, Ontario, Canada

Archetypical in its architecture of what a nation's capital
should look like, the city of Ottawa is on the Ottawa
River which divides Quebec and Ontario Provinces.
Visually exciting, the city blends its British and Canadian
heritages to allow the visitor a sampling of the old and
the new. The Parliament Buildings are the center of
historic interest, the oldest having been constructed a
little over 100 years ago, and the newest 57 years ago.
The National Arts Centre is a showcase for Ottawa's
avant-garde theatre and performing arts. Canada's artists
are well represented at the National Gallery of Canada.
Bi-cultural Quebec Province offers superb French cuisine,
good skiing and many historical sites. The Laurentians
offer mountain climbing, backpacking, skiing and just
simply walking.

ACCOMMODATIONS
Single room — $9.00 per person per day for adults
$4.00 per person per day for students
Double room — $7.00 per person per day
Suite — $12.00 per person per day
Pets are not permitted.
Accommodations are available to students, alumni, adults
and families.

MEALS
Cafeteria (typical prices)
Breakfast — $1.25
Lunch — $1.50
Dinner — $2.25
A coffee shop is available.

ACTIVITIES (on campus or nearby)
Swimming, hiking, fishing, skiing, tennis and mountain
climbing. Nominal fees are charged for swimming and
tennis. The Tulip Festival takes place in mid-May;
the Highland Games, the first of July; and Festival
Canada, the month of July.

AVAILABLE DATES
May 6 — August 20
Advance reservations are required.

CONTACT
Mr. Jean Hamel
Conventions Manager
235 Nicholas Street
Telephone: (613) 231-5058

CENTRE FOR CHRISTIAN STUDIES
Toronto, Ontario, Canada

A busy metropolis on Lake Ontario, Toronto is the gateway to the fascinating vacationlands stretching north in the Province of Ontario. It's an easy city in which to travel. Points of interest include the striking City Hall, Casa Loma Castle, Fort York, MacKenzie House, the Marine Museum, Ontario Science Center and the Royal Ontario Museum. High Park and the lakefront Ontario Place are attractive outdoor recreational centers.

ACCOMMODATIONS
Single room — $7.00 per person per day;
$38.00 per person per week
Double room — $6.00 per person per day;
$33.00 per person per week
All rates are subject to change without notice.
Baths are shared. Pets and children under 12 years of age are not permitted.
Accommodations are available to students, alumni, adults and families.

MEALS
Restaurants and coffee shop are in the area.

ACTIVITIES (on campus or nearby)
Area attractions are the University of Toronto, near downtown and public transportation to many points of interest in the area.

AVAILABLE DATES
May 1 — August 31
Advance reservations are required.

CONTACT
Mrs. Kay Pearson
77 Charles Street West
Telephone: (416) 923-1168

LOYOLA COLLEGE
Montreal, Quebec, Canada

Montreal is a city rich in French traditions, architecture, culture, higher education and fine cuisine. "Man and His World," first produced for the 1967 World's Fair, is now a permanent attraction. Montreal will extend its hospitality to the Olympic games in 1976. Old Montreal is one of the best examples of historical restoration in North America. It's a major seaport on the St. Lawrence Seaway, which flows south into Lake Ontario. Quebec is but a two-hour drive along the St. Lawrence. The Laurentian Mountains, north of Montreal, provide one of the finest summer resort and skiing areas in Canada.

ACCOMMODATIONS
Single room — $5.00 per person per day;
$25.00 per person per week
Double Room — $5.00 per person per day;
$25.00 per person per week
Baths are shared or private. Pets are not permitted. Accommodations are available to students, alumni, adults, families and prospective matriculants.

MEALS
Cafeteria (typical prices)
Breakfast — $ .85
Lunch — $1.45
Dinner — $1.65
A coffee shop is available.

ACTIVITIES (on campus or nearby)
Skiing, boating, tennis, swimming, theater, concerts, opera, ballet, bicycling and water-skiing. The Campus Centre at Loyola offers its conference room, stereo rooms and lounges. No fees are charged for campus sports activities.

AVAILABLE DATES
May 20 — August 18
Advance reservations are required.

CONTACT
Mr. Peter Brown, Director of Residence Life
101 Hingston Hall
7141 Sherbrooke Street, West
Telephone: (514) 482-0320, extensions 528, 529

McGILL UNIVERSITY
Montreal, Quebec, Canada

Montreal is a city of contrasts—of ultra-modernism side-by-side with mementos of the French explorers who first settled it. The Champlain Bridge, the skyscraper towers of modern buildings with a bee-hive activity veritably an underground city, a beautiful new subway—all juxtapose with "Old City" structures dating back hundreds of years. Over 1,100 miles from the Atlantic on the St. Lawrence River, Montreal is a great seaport and Canada's largest city. More than two-thirds of the people speak French The residences of the University are located on the slopes of Mount Royal, with its 531-acre Mount Royal Park. With all of this you have the Laurentians, the playground of the province for a backdrop.

ACCOMMODATIONS
Single room—$9.50 per person per day
(room and breakfast)
$13.50 per person per day (room and board)
$8.50 per person per day (room and breakfast
for students and academics)
$11.50 per person per day (room and board for students
and academics)
Baths are shared. Linens and maid service are included. Accommodations are available to students, alumni, adults, families and prospective matriculants.

MEALS
Cafeteria (typical prices)
Breakfast — $1.35
Lunch — $1.65
Dinner — $2.15

ACTIVITIES (on campus or nearby)
Tennis, swimming, fishing and hiking. Picnics, weekend trips and guided scenic tours are available through Montreal tourist centers. Historic "Old Montreal," museums, parks and cultural activities. Tents, canoes and backpacks are available for rent.

AVAILABLE DATES
May 15—August 31
Advance reservations are required.

CONTACT
Mr. Charles H. Rannells
3935 University Street
Telephone: (514) 392-4224

MONTREAL UNIVERSITY
Montreal, Quebec, Canada

Montreal is a city of contrasts — of ultra-modernism side-by-side with mementos of the French explorers who first settled it. The Champlain Bridge, the skyscraper towers of modern buildings with a bee-hive activity veritably an underground city, a beautiful new subway — all juxtapose with "Old City" structures dating back hundreds of years. Over 1,100 miles from the Atlantic on the St. Laurence River, Montreal is a great seaport and Canada's largest city. More than two-thirds of the people speak Franch. The residences of the University are located on the slopes of Mount Royal, with its 531-acre Mount Royal Park. With all of this you have the Laurentians, the playground of the province for a backdrop.

ACCOMMODATIONS
The following are the 1974 rates. The 1975 rates are not yet available.
Single room — $4.00 to $6.00 per student per day;
$15.00 to $18.00 per student per week;
$8.00 to $10.00 per adult per day
Double room — $3.00 to $5.00 per student per day;
$13.00 to $15.00 per student per week;
$6.00 to $8.00 per adult per day
Pets are not permitted.
Accommodations are available to students, alumni, adults, prospective matriculants and groups.

MEALS
Cafeteria (typical prices)
Breakfast — $1.25
Lunch — $2.00
Dinner — $2.00

ACTIVITIES (on campus or nearby)
Tennis, hiking, boating, swimming and water sports.

AVAILABLE DATES
May 15 — August 15
Advance reservations are required.

CONTACT
Miss Lise Julien
2350 Edward Montpetit Boulevard
P.O. Box 6128
Telephone: (514) 343-6531

UNIVERSITY OF SASKATCHEWAN
LUTHERAN THEOLOGICAL SEMINARY
Saskatoon, Saskatchewan, Canada

The Province of Saskatchewan has long been a melting pot for middle-European farmers to whom the Great Plains area of Canada, rich in oats, wheat and flax, has brought prosperity. The city of Saskatoon is named after the bush, saskatoon, which bears savory purple berries. One-half of the world's reserve of potash, an important natural resource, is mined in the Saskatoon area.
A cultural complex, including a theatre and conservatory, also houses the Mendel Art Gallery and its excellent collection of Canadian and Eskimo art. The Saskachimo Exposition, a two-week fair in July, re-enacts local and province history.

ACCOMMODATIONS
Single room — $12.00 per person per day;
$60.00 per person per week (includes meals)
Pets are not permitted.
Accommodations are available to students, alumni and adults.

MEALS
There is no set cost for meals. A cafeteria is available.

ACTIVITIES (on campus or nearby)
Swimming, tennis, Western Development Museum, Marquis Downs Race Track, Forestry Farm Park, Gardiner Dam and Lake Diefenbaker, and Batonche National Historic Park.

AVAILABLE DATES
May 31 — August 31
Advance reservations are required.

CONTACT
Mr. P. T. Paulsen
Business Administrator
Telephone: (306) 343-8204, extension 3

Now, get in on the world's second best kept secret. You're invited to over 7,000 parties — festivals, feasts, fairs, and fiestas once you get where you're going.

Pick a Month. Pick a Spot. MORT'S FESTIVAL GUIDES tell you where the parties are. All the popular festivals are here: Jazz and dance. Film and theatre. Sports, music and seafood. Opera, folk and Shakespeare. Days of wine, food, beer and roses. There are unusual, exotic, and amusing celebrations which you may never have heard of. Rattlesnake Roundups. Mule Days. Getting Out of Red Flannel Underwear Contests. Camel and Ostrich Races. National Cow Chip Throwing Festivals and Ugliest Fish Other Than Smelts Contests. All listed in MORT'S FESTIVAL GUIDES which tell you when and where to go for Chinese New Year celebrations. Mexican Carnivals and Stampedes. Jousting Tourneys and Oktoberfests. Rennaissance Fairs and thousands more. Each section of the world has its own index, so you can put your finger on the activity which catches your fancy.